The Open University

MT365 Graphs, network

Graphs 1

Graphs and digraphs

Study guide

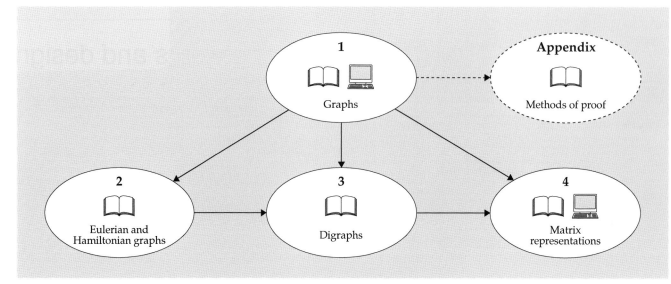

Section 1 is about twice the length of each of the other sections, and you should expect to spend more time on it than on the others. The material in this section is straightforward but fundamental to your understanding of the *Graphs* units, and you should make sure that you become familiar with it. The material in Sections 2, 3 and 4 is also straightforward. In particular, much of Section 3 is simply an adaptation to digraphs of some of the material of Sections 1 and 2, and you may prefer simply to skim through it, referring back to it later if you need to.

Each section contains a number of case studies, which you can read either after studying the appropriate underlying theoretical material or at the end of the section. They are chosen to illustrate the wide range of topics to which graph theory has been applied. *Only a few of these case studies are assessed each year; those case studies that do not appear in the first TMA or CMA are not assessed.* None of the case studies is assessed in the examination.

Included in this unit is an Appendix on methods of proof, set in the context of graph theory. You need read this Appendix only if you are unfamiliar with the topics it covers. It may be studied any time after Section 1.

There are computer activities associated with Sections 1 and 4.

There is no audio-tape or television programme associated with this unit.

The Open University, Walton Hall, Milton Keynes, MK7 6AA.

First published 1995. Reprinted 1997, 2000, 2002, 2003, 2005, 2008, 2009.

Copyright © 1995 The Open University

Printed and bound by Page Bros, Norwich.

ISBN 0 7492 2220 4

1.6

Contents

Introduction

In the previous unit, *Introduction*, you saw how graphs and digraphs can be used to model the relationships between certain objects. Such a model consists of a pictorial representation in which the objects are represented by points and the relationships are represented by lines joining them in pairs. When the relationships are two-way, we obtain a *graph* consisting of vertices and edges; when they are one-way, we obtain a *digraph* consisting of vertices and arcs. We regard different pictures representing the same relationships as the same graph or digraph.

Much of the interest and importance of graph theory arises from its use in the modelling of various situations, and the course contains many examples of this modelling process. However, in order to investigate such situations, we shall need to study graphs and digraphs in some detail, and this is the aim of the four *Graphs* units.

Our aim in this unit is to prepare the ground for such a programme by introducing some basic terminology that will be needed throughout the course.

We start, in Section 1, *Graphs*, by reminding you of some of the concepts we introduced in the previous unit, and by introducing some definitions and examples that will play an important role in what follows. The case studies in this section arise from recreational mathematics, chemistry, music and the social sciences.

Much of the material in Section 2, *Eulerian and Hamiltonian graphs*, originally arose from mathematical puzzles, although it is increasingly being used in practical situations. The basic idea is to find a route which visits each edge or vertex of a given graph just once and returns to the starting point; an example of this is the Königsberg bridges problem. The case studies in this section arise from recreational mathematics and coding theory.

In Section 3, *Digraphs*, we present analogues for digraphs of the graph definitions and examples in Sections 1 and 2. The case studies in this section arise from ecology, the social sciences, telecommunications and statistics.

Finally, in Section 4, *Matrix representations*, we show how matrices can be used to represent graphs and digraphs. The case studies on matrices arise from archaeology, genetics and statistics.

1   Graphs

The intuitive idea of a graph is already familiar to you from the *Introduction* unit. In this section we treat the subject more formally, introducing the basic definitions and examples that will be needed throughout the course.

1.1   Graphs and subgraphs

We start by formalizing the definition of a *graph*.

Definitions

A **graph** consists of a set of elements called **vertices** and a set of elements called **edges**. Each edge is associated with two vertices, and is said to **join** them.

For example, the graph shown has four vertices $\{u, v, w, x\}$ and six edges $\{1, 2, 3, 4, 5, 6\}$. Edge 1 joins the vertices u and x, edge 2 joins the vertices u and w, edges 3 and 4 join the vertices v and w, edge 5 joins the vertices w and x, and edge 6 joins the vertex x to itself.

We often denote an edge by specifying its two vertices: for example, edge 1 can be denoted by ux or xu, edges 3 and 4 can be denoted by vw or wv, and edge 6 can be denoted by xx.

Note that the above graph contains more than one edge joining the vertices v and w, and an edge joining the vertex x to itself. The following terminology is useful when discussing such graphs.

Definitions

In a graph, two or more edges joining the same pair of vertices are **multiple edges**. An edge joining a vertex to itself is a **loop**.

A graph with no loops or multiple edges is a **simple graph**.

For example, graph (a) below has multiple edges and graph (b) has a loop, so neither is a simple graph. Graph (c) has no loops or multiple edges, and is therefore a simple graph.

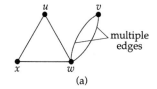
(a)

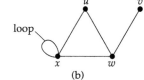
(b)

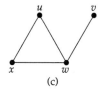
(c)

Problem 1.1 ——————————————————————

Write down the vertices and edges of each of the following graphs. Are these graphs simple graphs?

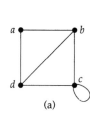
(a)

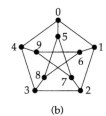
(b)

Problem 1.2 ——————————————————————

Draw the graphs whose vertices and edges are as follows. Are these graphs simple graphs?

(a)   vertices: $\{u, v, w, x\}$ edges: $\{uv, vw, vx, wx\}$

(b)   vertices: $\{1, 2, 3, 4, 5, 6, 7, 8\}$ edges: $\{12, 22, 23, 34, 35, 67, 68, 78\}$

Adjacency and incidence

Since graph theory is primarily concerned with relationships between objects, it is convenient to introduce some further terminology that indicates when certain vertices and edges occur next to each other in a graph.

Definitions

The vertices v and w of a graph are **adjacent** vertices if they are joined by an edge e. The vertices v and w are **incident** with the edge e, and the edge e is **incident** with the vertices v and w.

For example, in the graph below, vertices u and x are adjacent, vertex w is incident with edges 2, 3, 4 and 5, and edge 6 is incident with vertex x.

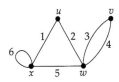

Problem 1.3

Which of the following statements hold for the graph on the right?

(a) vertices v and w are adjacent;

(b) vertices v and x are adjacent;

(c) vertex u is incident with edge 2;

(d) edge 5 is incident with vertex x.

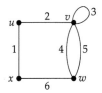

Isomorphism

It follows from the definition that a graph is completely determined when we know its vertices and edges, and that two graphs are *the same* if they have the same vertices and edges. Once we know the vertices and edges, we can draw the graph and, in principle, any picture we draw is as good as any other; the actual way in which the vertices and edges are drawn is irrelevant.

For example, recall the *utilities graph*, in which three neighbours A, B and C are joined to the three utilities gas, water and electricity. This graph may be described completely by the following sets:

> We met this graph in the *Introduction* unit, Section 3.

vertices: $\{A, B, C, g, w, e\}$,
edges: $\{Ag, Aw, Ae, Bg, Bw, Be, Cg, Cw, Ce\}$;

> We use g, w and e to denote gas, water and electricity, respectively.

and can be drawn in many ways, such as the following:

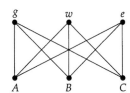 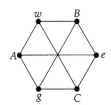

Each of these diagrams has six vertices and nine edges, and each conveys the same information — that each neighbour is joined to each utility, but that no two neighbours are joined and no two utilities are joined. It follows that these two dissimilar diagrams represent the same graph.

On the other hand, two diagrams may look similar but represent different graphs. For example, the diagrams below look similar, but they do not represent the same graph, since, for example, AB is an edge of the second graph but not the first.

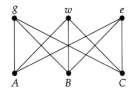 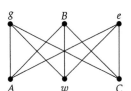

We express this similarity by saying that the graphs represented by these two diagrams are *isomorphic*. This means that *the two graphs have essentially the same structure*: we can relabel the vertices in the first graph to get the second one — in this case, we simply interchange the labels w and B. Similarly, the graphs G and H represented by the diagrams

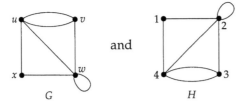

and

are not the same, but they are isomorphic, since we can relabel the vertices in the graph G to get the graph H, using the following one–one correspondence:

G:	u	v	w	x
	↕	↕	↕	↕
H:	4	3	2	1

Note that edges in G correspond to edges in H — for example:

the two edges between u and v in G correspond to the two edges between 4 and 3 in H;

the edge uw in G corresponds to the edge 42 in H;

the loop ww in G corresponds to the loop 22 in H;

and so on.

This leads to the following definition.

Definition

Two graphs G and H are **isomorphic** if H can be obtained by relabelling the vertices of G — that is, if there is a one–one correspondence between the vertices of G and those of H such that the number of edges joining each pair of vertices in G is equal to the number of edges joining the corresponding pair of vertices in H.

Note that, in checking whether two graphs are *the same*, we must check carefully whether all the vertex labels correspond. However, in checking whether two graphs are *isomorphic*, we need to investigate whether we can relabel the vertices of one graph to give those of the other. In order to do this, we first check that the graphs have the same numbers of vertices and edges, and then look for special features in the two graphs, such as a loop, multiple edges, or the number of edges meeting at a vertex. For example, the following two graphs both have five vertices and six edges, but are not isomorphic, as the first has two vertices where just two edges meet, whereas the second has only one.

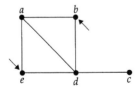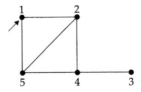

Problem 1.4 ───────────────────────────────

By suitably relabelling the vertices, show that the following pairs of graphs are isomorphic:

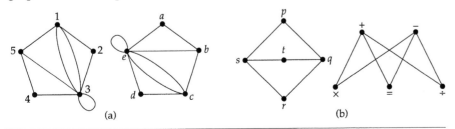

(a)   (b)

Problem 1.5

Are the following two graphs isomorphic? If so, find a suitable one–one correspondence between the vertices of the first and those of the second; if not, explain why no such one–one correspondence exists.

For some problems, it is not necessary to have labels on the graphs. In such cases, we can omit the labels and refer to the resulting object as an *unlabelled graph*. For example, the unlabelled graph

corresponds to either of the following isomorphic graphs:

Indeed, it also corresponds to either of the following graphs, which are isomorphic to the above two:

We say that two unlabelled graphs such as

 and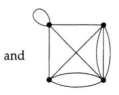

are *isomorphic* if labels can be attached to their vertices so that they become the same graph.

Problem 1.6

By suitably labelling the vertices, show that the following unlabelled graphs are isomorphic:

From now on, we use the term *graph* to indicate either a graph with labels on the vertices and/or edges, or an unlabelled graph. The meaning will usually be clear from the context, but if there is any possibility of confusion, we shall insert the word *labelled* or *unlabelled*, as appropriate.

Subgraphs

It is a common feature of both mathematics and technology that we study complicated objects by looking at simpler objects of the same type contained in them — subsets of sets, subsystems of systems, subgroups of groups, and so on. In graph theory we make the following definition.

> **Definition**
>
> A **subgraph** of a graph G is a graph all of whose vertices are vertices of G and all of whose edges are edges of G.

Note that G is a subgraph of G.

For example, if G is the graph on the left below, with vertices $\{u, v, w, x\}$ and edges $\{1, 2, 3, 4, 5\}$, then the following are all subgraphs of G:

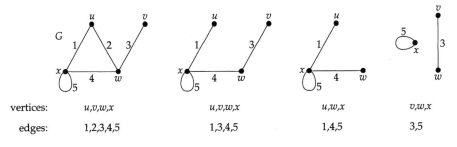

vertices:	u,v,w,x	u,v,w,x	u,w,x	v,w,x
edges:	1,2,3,4,5	1,3,4,5	1,4,5	3,5

Problem 1.7

Which of the graphs (a), (b) and (c) are subgraphs of the graph G below?

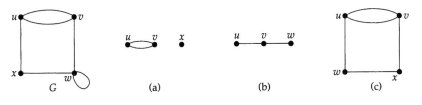

The idea of a subgraph can be extended to unlabelled graphs. For example, if H is the unlabelled graph shown on the left below, then the unlabelled graphs (a), (b) and (c) are all subgraphs of H:

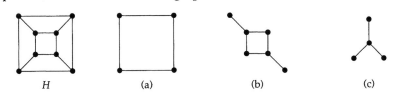

The configuration in graph (c) occurs at each corner of H.

Problem 1.8

Which of the graphs (a), (b) and (c) are subgraphs of the graph H below?

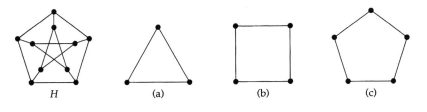

Counting graphs

We conclude this subsection by indicating the relative numbers of labelled and unlabelled graphs.

When counting *labelled* graphs, we distinguish between any two that are not *the same*. For example, there are just eight different labelled simple graphs with three vertices:

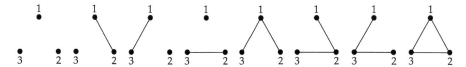

When counting *unlabelled* graphs, we distinguish between any two that are not *isomorphic*. For example, there are just four different unlabelled simple graphs with three vertices:

The following table lists the numbers of labelled and unlabelled simple graphs with up to eight vertices:

n	1	2	3	4	5	6	7	8
labelled graphs	1	2	8	64	1024	32 768	2 097 152	268 435 456
unlabelled graphs	1	2	4	11	34	156	1044	12 346

Notice how fast these numbers grow. This is an example of the *combinatorial explosion* (see the *Introduction* unit).

In general, counting problems for labelled graphs are much easier to solve than their counterparts for unlabelled graphs. In fact, there are certain types of graph for which the former problems have been solved while the latter remain unsolved.

Historical note

In 1935, the Hungarian mathematician Georg Pólya obtained a general formula from which one can calculate the number of unlabelled graphs with any given number of vertices and edges. Pólya's methods have since been applied to several other graph-counting problems.

Problem 1.9

Draw the eleven unlabelled simple graphs with four vertices.

If you wish, you can now proceed directly to Section 1.5 and read Case study (a), *The four-cubes problem*.

1.2   Vertex degrees in graphs

In many applications of graph theory we need a term for the number of edges meeting at a vertex. For example, we may wish to specify the number of roads meeting at a particular road intersection, the number of wires meeting at a given terminal of an electrical network, or the number of chemical bonds joining a given atom to its neighbours. These situations are illustrated below:

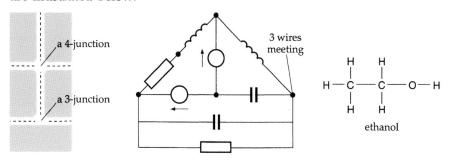

In chemistry the term *valency* is used to indicate the number of bonds connecting an atom to its neighbours. For example, a carbon atom C has valency 4, an oxygen atom O has valency 2, and a hydrogen atom H has valency 1, as illustrated in the above diagram representing the molecule *ethanol*. For graphs, we usually use the word *degree*.

Definition

In a graph, the **degree** of a vertex v is the number of edges incident with v, with each loop counted twice, and is denoted by **deg** v.

Each loop contributes 2 to the degree of a vertex because it has two ends joined to that vertex.

For example, graph (a) below has vertex degrees

$$\deg u = 2, \quad \deg v = 1, \quad \deg w = 4, \quad \deg x = 3, \quad \deg y = 0,$$

and graph (b) has vertex degrees

$$\deg u = 2, \quad \deg v = 5, \quad \deg w = 4, \quad \deg x = 5, \quad \deg y = 0.$$

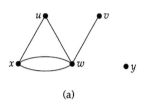   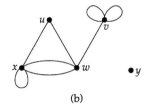

        (a)   (b)

We sometimes need to list the degrees of all the vertices in a graph, and this is usually done by writing them down in increasing order, with 'repeats' where necessary. Accordingly, we make the following definition.

Definition

The **degree sequence** of a graph G is the sequence obtained by listing the vertex degrees of G in increasing order, with repeats as necessary.

For example:

graph (a) above has degree sequence $(0, 1, 2, 3, 4)$;

graph (b) above has degree sequence $(0, 2, 4, 5, 5)$.

Problem 1.10 ——————————————————————

Write down the degree sequence of each of the following graphs:

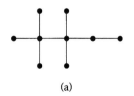   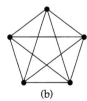   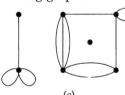

     (a)   (b)   (c)

Problem 1.11 ——————————————————————

For each of the graphs in Problem 1.10, write down the number of edges and the sum of the degrees of all the vertices. What is the connection between your answers? Can you explain why this connection arises?

The handshaking lemma

In the solution to Problem 1.11, you should have noticed that the sum of the vertex degrees of each graph is exactly twice the number of edges. A corresponding result holds for all graphs, and is usually called the *handshaking lemma*.

Theorem 1.1: handshaking lemma

In any graph, the sum of all the vertex degrees is equal to twice the number of edges.

Proof

Since each edge has two ends, it must contribute exactly 2 to the sum of the vertex degrees. The result follows immediately. ∎

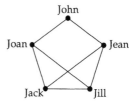

The name *handshaking lemma* arises from the fact that a graph can be used to represent a group of people shaking hands. In such a graph, the vertices represent the people and an edge appears whenever the corresponding people have shaken hands. With this interpretation, the number of edges represents the total number of handshakes, the degree of a vertex is the number of hands shaken by the corresponding person, and the sum of the degrees is the total number of hands shaken. The handshaking lemma states that the total number of hands shaken is twice the number of handshakes — the reason is, of course, that exactly two hands are involved in each handshake.

Historical note

The handshaking lemma first appeared (in a different form) in a paper of Leonhard Euler (1707–1783), entitled *Solutio problematis ad geometriam situs pertinentis* (The solution of a problem relating to the geometry of position). This important paper, widely regarded as 'the earliest paper in graph theory', dates from 1736, and contains Euler's solution of the Königsberg bridges problem.

Problem 1.12 ────────────────────────────────

(a) Use the handshaking lemma to prove that, in any graph, the number of vertices of odd degree is even.

(b) Verify that the result of part (a) holds for each of the graphs in Problem 1.10.

Regular graphs

If all the vertex degrees in a graph are the same, we give the graph a particular name.

Definitions

A graph is **regular** if its vertices all have the same degree.

A regular graph is **r-regular**, or **regular of degree r**, if the degree of each vertex is r.

In the following diagrams we illustrate some r-regular graphs, for various values of r:

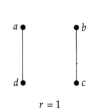

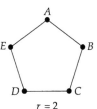

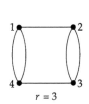

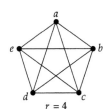

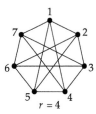

Problem 1.13

Draw an r-regular graph with eight vertices when:

(a) $r = 3$;   (b) $r = 4$;   (c) $r = 5$.

A useful consequence of the handshaking lemma is the following result.

Theorem 1.2

Let G be an r-regular graph with n vertices; then G has exactly $nr/2$ edges.

Proof

There are n vertices, each of degree r, so the sum of the degrees of all the vertices is nr. By the handshaking lemma, the number of edges is one-half of this amount, which is $nr/2$. ∎

Problem 1.14

Verify Theorem 1.2 for each of the following regular graphs:

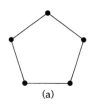

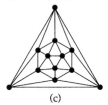

(a)   (b)   (c)

Problem 1.15

(a)   Prove that there are no 3-regular graphs with seven vertices.

(b)   Prove that, if n and r are both odd, then there are no r-regular graphs with n vertices.

Examples of regular graphs

We now consider some important classes of regular graphs.

Complete graphs

A **complete graph** is a graph in which each vertex is joined to each of the others by exactly one edge.

The complete graph with n vertices is denoted by K_n.

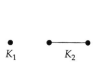

Note that K_n is regular of degree $n-1$, and therefore has $n(n-1)/2$ edges, by Theorem 1.2.

Null graphs

A **null graph** is a graph with no edges.

The null graph with n vertices is denoted by N_n.

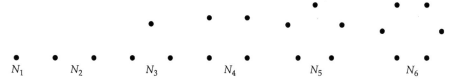

Note that N_n is regular of degree 0.

Cycle graphs

A **cycle graph** is a graph consisting of a single cycle of vertices and edges.

The cycle graph with n vertices is denoted by C_n.

You met the idea of a *cycle* in the *Introduction* unit. It is defined formally in Section 1.3.

For $n \geq 3$, C_n can be drawn in the form of a regular n-gon.

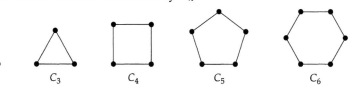

Note that C_n is regular of degree 2, and has n edges.

Problem 1.16

Draw the graphs K_7, N_7 and C_7. How many edges does each have?

The Platonic graphs

The following five regular solids are known as the *Platonic solids*:

The name 'Platonic' arises from the fact that these solids were mentioned in Plato's *Timaeus*. The solids are listed in the order of the number of vertices in the corresponding graph.

   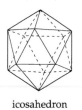 

tetrahedron   octahedron   cube   icosahedron   dodecahedron

We can regard the vertices and edges of each solid as the vertices and edges of a regular graph. The resulting five graphs are known as the **Platonic graphs**, and are often drawn as follows:

tetrahedron   octahedron   cube   icosahedron   dodecahedron

The tetrahedron, cube and dodecahedron graphs are 3-regular, the octahedron graph is 4-regular and the icosahedron graph is 5-regular.

The Petersen graph

Our last example of a regular graph is known as the **Petersen graph**, named after the Danish mathematician Julius Petersen. It has several interesting properties, as you will discover as the course progresses. The Petersen graph may be drawn in various ways, two of which are:

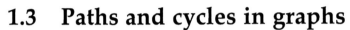

The Petersen graph is a 3-regular graph with 10 vertices and 15 edges.

If you wish, you can now proceed directly to Section 1.5 and read Case study (b), *Chemistry*.

JULIUS PETERSEN (1839–1910)

Julius Petersen was an important figure in Danish mathematics. He became professor of mathematics in Copenhagen, and was nationally known as the author of a series of school and undergraduate textbooks. He discussed the graph named after him in a paper of 1898.

1.3   Paths and cycles in graphs

Many applications of graphs involve 'getting from one vertex to another'. For example, you may wish to find the shortest route between one town and another. Other examples include the routeing of a telephone call between one subscriber and another, the flow of current between two terminals of an electrical network, and the tracing of a maze. We now make this idea precise. We start by defining a *walk* in a graph.

Definition

A **walk of length k** in a graph is a succession of k edges of the form

$uv, vw, wx, \ldots , yz.$

We denote this walk by $uvwx\ldots yz$, and refer to it as a **walk between u and z**.

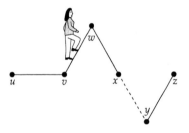

We can think of such a walk as being from u to v, then from v to w, then from w to x, and so on, until we arrive eventually at the vertex z. Since the edges are undirected, we can also think of it as a walk from z to y and on, eventually, to x, w, v and u. So we can equally well denote this walk by $zy\ldots xwvu$, and refer to it as a walk between z and u.

Note that we do not require all the edges or vertices in a walk to be different. For example, in the graph shown, $uvwxywvzzy$ is a walk of length 9 between the vertices u and y that includes the edge vw twice and the vertices v, w, y and z twice.

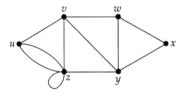

Paths, trails and connected graphs

It is sometimes useful to be able to refer to more restrictive conditions in which we require all the edges, or all the vertices, in a walk to be different.

Definitions

A **trail** is a walk in which all the edges (but not necessarily all the vertices) are different.

A **path** is a trail in which all the vertices are different.

In the graph above, the walk $vzzywxy$ is a trail that is not a path (since the vertices y and z both occur twice), whereas the walk $vwxyz$ has no repeated vertices and is therefore a path.

Problem 1.17

Complete the following statements concerning the graph on the right:

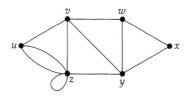

(a) *xyzzvy* is a .... of length ...... between ..... and ..... ;

(b) *uvyz* is a .... of length ...... between ..... and ..... .

Problem 1.18

Write down all the paths between *s* and *y* in the following graph:

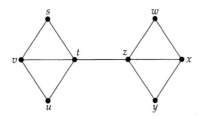

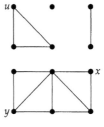

We can use the concept of a path to define a *connected graph*. Intuitively, a graph is said to be *connected* if it is 'in one piece'; for example, the graph in the margin is not connected, but consists of four connected subgraphs. The observation that there is a path between *x* and *y* (which lie in the same subgraph), but not between *u* and *y* (which lie in different subgraphs), leads us to make the following definitions.

Definitions

A graph is **connected** if there is a path between each pair of vertices, and is **disconnected** otherwise.

Every disconnected graph can be split up into a number of connected subgraphs, called **components**.

For example, the following disconnected graph has three components:

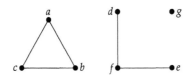

Problem 1.19

(a) Draw a connected graph with eight vertices.

(b) Draw a disconnected graph with eight vertices and two components.

(c) Draw a disconnected graph with eight vertices and three components.

Closed trails and cycles

It is also useful to have a special term for those walks or trails that start and finish at the same vertex. We say that they are *closed*.

Note that a path with at least one edge cannot be closed.

Definitions

A **closed walk** in a graph is a succession of edges of the form

   uv, vw, wx, ... , yz, zu.

A **closed trail** is a closed walk in which all the edges are different.

A **cycle** is a closed trail in which all the intermediate vertices are different.

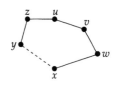

In the graph below, the closed walk *vywxyzv* is a closed trail that is not a cycle, whereas the closed trails *zz*, *vwxyv* and *vwxyzv* are all cycles. A cycle of length 3, such as *vwyv* or *wxyw*, is called a *triangle*. In describing closed walks, we can allow any vertex to be the starting vertex. For example, the triangle *vwyv* can equally well be specified by the letters *wyvw* or *yvwy* or (since the direction is immaterial) by *vywv*, *wvyw* or *ywvy*.

A walk or trail is *open* if it starts and finishes at different vertices.

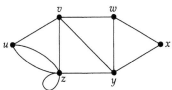

Problem 1.20

For the graph on the right, write down:

(a) a closed walk that is not a closed trail;

(b) a closed trail that is not a cycle;

(c) all the cycles of lengths 1, 2, 3 and 4.

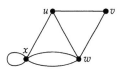

> If you wish, you can now proceed directly to Section 1.5 and read Case study (c), *Music*.

1.4 Bipartite graphs

Of particular importance in applications are the bipartite graphs.

Definition

A **bipartite graph** is a graph whose set of vertices can be split into two sets A and B in such a way that each edge of the graph joins a vertex in A to a vertex in B.

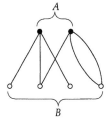

We can distinguish the vertices in A from those in B by drawing the former in black and the latter in white, so that each edge is incident with a black vertex and a white vertex. Two examples of bipartite graphs are:

 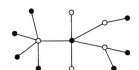

Problem 1.21

Prove that, in a bipartite graph, any cycle has even length.

We ask you to prove the converse of this in Exercise 1.8.

Examples of bipartite graphs

As with regular graphs, there are several important classes of bipartite graphs.

Complete bipartite graphs

A **complete bipartite graph** is a bipartite graph in which each vertex in A is joined to each vertex in B by just one edge.

The complete bipartite graph with r black vertices in A and s white vertices in B is denoted by $K_{r,s}$. Some examples of complete bipartite graphs are:

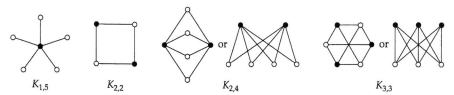

Note that $K_{r,s}$ is the same as $K_{s,r}$ (exchange the roles of A and B) and has $r + s$ vertices (r vertices of degree s and s vertices of degree r) and rs edges.

Problem 1.22

(a) Draw the graphs $K_{2,3}$, $K_{1,7}$ and $K_{4,4}$. How many vertices and edges does each have?

(b) Under what conditions on r and s is $K_{r,s}$ a regular graph?

Trees

One of the most important classes of bipartite graphs is the class of *trees*. A **tree** is a connected graph with no cycles. Some examples of trees are:

Note that

in a tree, there is just one path between each pair of vertices.

We can see this as follows. Since a tree is connected, there is at least one path between each pair of vertices. However, there cannot be two paths between any two vertices, because this would create a cycle, contrary to our definition of a tree.

Such a cycle may include all of the edges in both paths or only some of them:

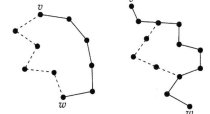

Problem 1.23

There are eight unlabelled trees with five or fewer vertices. Draw them.

Problem 1.24

(a) By colouring alternate vertices black and white, explain why every tree is a bipartite graph.

   Hint   Use the fact that there is just one path between each pair of vertices of a tree.

(b) Explain why a tree with n vertices must have $n - 1$ edges.

Path graphs

A **path graph** is a tree in which there is a path that passes through all its vertices.

The path graph with n vertices is denoted by P_n.

Note that P_n has $n - 1$ edges, and is obtained from the cycle graph C_n by removing any edge.

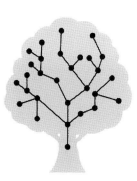

Cubes

Of particular interest among the bipartite graphs are the *cubes*. They have important applications in coding theory, and may be constructed by taking as vertices all binary words (sequences of 0s and 1s) of a given length and joining two of these vertices whenever the corresponding sequences differ in just one place. The graph obtained in this way from the binary words of length k is called the **k-cube** (or **k-dimensional cube**), and is denoted by Q_k.

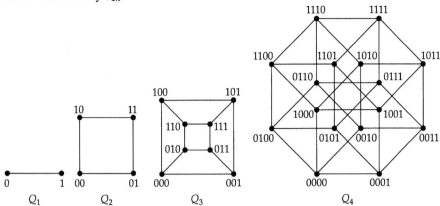

Note that Q_k has 2^k vertices, and is regular of degree k. It follows from Theorem 1.2 that Q_k has $2^{k-1}k$ edges.

> If you wish, you can now proceed directly to Section 1.5 and read Case study (d), *Social networks*.

1.5   Case studies

We conclude this section by introducing four case studies — the four-cubes problem, chemistry, music and social networks.

(a)   The four-cubes problem

An intriguing recreational puzzle, which has been marketed under the name of *Instant Insanity*, concerns four cubes whose faces are coloured red, blue, yellow and green. These cubes are depicted in flattened-out form below. The problem is *to pile the cubes on top of each other so that all four colours appear on each side of the resulting 'stack'*. As we shall see, there is essentially only one way in which this can be done for these cubes.

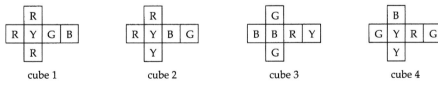

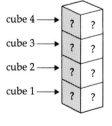

A trial-and-error approach to this problem is inadvisable, since there are thousands of different ways of stacking the cubes. To see this, note that each cube can be placed in twenty-four different ways, since there are six possible choices for the top face, and the cube can then be rotated so as to bring any of the four side faces to the front; thus, the total number of possible stacks is $24^4 = 331\,776$. This number can be reduced by a factor of 4 if we regard two stacks as the same when we can rotate one of them to get the other, but this still leaves us with $24^4/4 = 82\,944$ essentially different stacks.

Now, if one face of a cube appears on one side of the stack, then the opposite face of the cube must appear on the opposite side of the stack. It follows that our concern is with opposite pairs of faces, and that we must decide, for each cube, which two of the three opposite pairs should appear on the sides of the stack.

To solve this problem, we represent each cube by a graph that tells us which pairs of colours appear on opposite faces. More precisely, we represent each cube by a graph with four vertices R, B, Y, G (corresponding to the four colours) in which two vertices are adjacent when the cube in question has the corresponding colours on opposite faces. For example, in cube 1, blue and yellow appear on opposite faces, and so the vertices B and Y are joined in the corresponding graph. The graphs for the above set of cubes are given below; on the right we have superimposed them to give a new graph G.

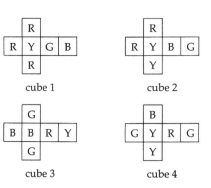

cube 1   cube 2

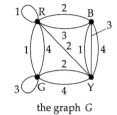

cube 3   cube 4

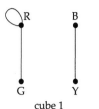

cube 1

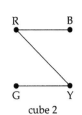

cube 2

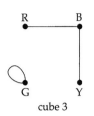

cube 3

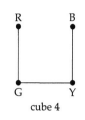

cube 4

the graph G

A solution of the four-cubes problem is obtained by finding two particular subgraphs H_1 and H_2 of G. The subgraph H_1 tells us which pair of colours appears on the front and back faces of each cube, and the subgraph H_2 tells us which pair of colours appears on the left-hand and right-hand faces of each cube. To do this, the subgraphs H_1 and H_2 must satisfy three properties:

(a) each contains exactly one edge from the graph for each cube;

(b) they have no edges in common;

(c) each vertex is incident with two edges.

Property (a) tells us that each cube has a front and a back, and a left side and a right side, and the subgraphs H_1 and H_2 tell us which pairs of colours appear on these faces. Property (b) tells us that the faces appearing on the front and back of a cube cannot be the same as those appearing on the sides. Property (c) tells us that each colour appears exactly twice on the sides of the stack (once on each side), and exactly twice on the front and back (once on the front and once on the back).

A solution to the four-cubes problem for the above set of cubes is shown below. In this solution, the subgraphs H_1 and H_2 tell us that cube 1 has yellow on the front and blue on the back (from H_1) and red on the left and green on the right (from H_2), and similarly for the other cubes.

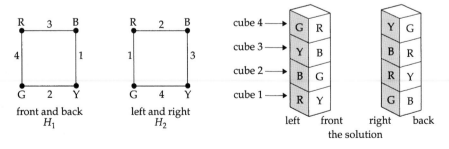

front and back
H_1

left and right
H_2

left front   right back
the solution

In Exercise 1.9 at the end of the unit, we ask you to show that, for the above set of cubes, the subgraphs H_1 and H_2 shown here are the only pair of subgraphs of G that satisfy properties (a), (b) and (c). This shows that this solution is the only one possible in this instance.

Problem 1.25 ─────────────────────────────

Use the above approach to solve the four-cubes problem for the following set of cubes:

cube 1

cube 2

cube 3

cube 4

(b) Chemistry

We have already seen in the *Introduction* unit that a molecule can be represented as a graph whose vertices correspond to the atoms and whose edges correspond to the bonds connecting them. For example, the molecule *ethanol*, with formula C_2H_5OH, can be represented by a graph as follows:

In such a graph, the degree of each vertex is simply the valency of the corresponding atom — the carbon vertices have degree 4, the oxygen vertex has degree 2, and the hydrogen vertices have degree 1.

Diagrams of the above type are used to represent the arrangement of atoms in a molecule. They explain the existence of *isomers* — molecules with the same formula but different properties. For example, the molecules n-butane and 2-methyl propane (formerly called butane and isobutane) both have the formula C_4H_{10}; but note the different ways in which the atoms are arranged inside the molecule:

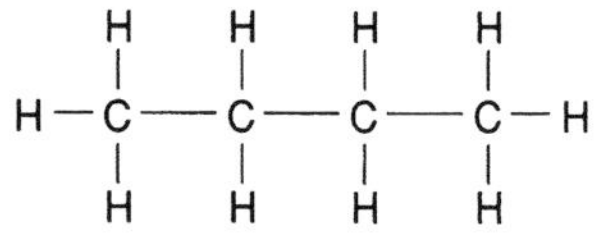

n-butane 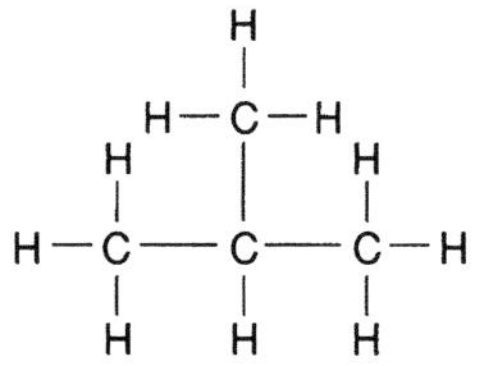   2-methyl propane

It is natural to ask whether there are any other molecules with the formula C_4H_{10}, and this leads us directly to the problem of *isomer enumeration* — the determination of the number of non-isomeric molecules with a given formula. The most celebrated problem of this kind is that of counting the alkanes (paraffins) C_nH_{2n+2}. For small values of n, we can construct a table, as on page 22, where for clarity the carbon vertices are drawn white.

It is clear that these diagrams are going to become very complicated as n increases. We can simplify them considerably by removing all the hydrogen atoms, as follows:

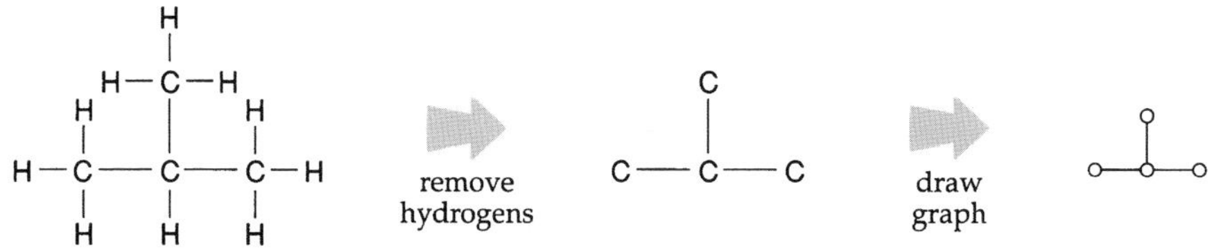

This leaves the following non-isomorphic *carbon graphs* with up to five carbon atoms:

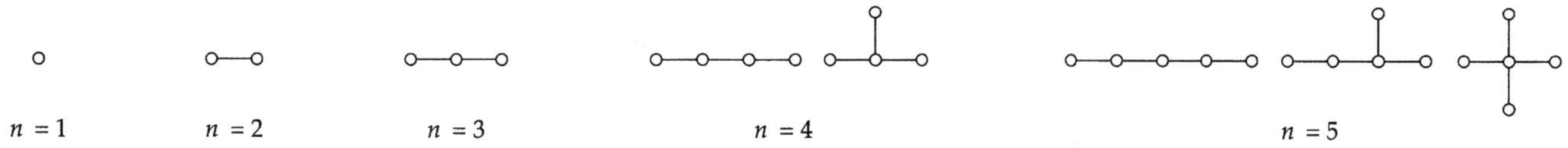

$n = 1$ $n = 2$ $n = 3$ $n = 4$ $n = 5$

Each of these carbon graphs has a tree-like structure in which each vertex has degree 4 or less. Conversely, from any tree with this property, we can construct an alkane by adding enough hydrogen atoms to bring the degree of each carbon vertex up to 4, as follows:

Trees are discussed in Section 1.4.

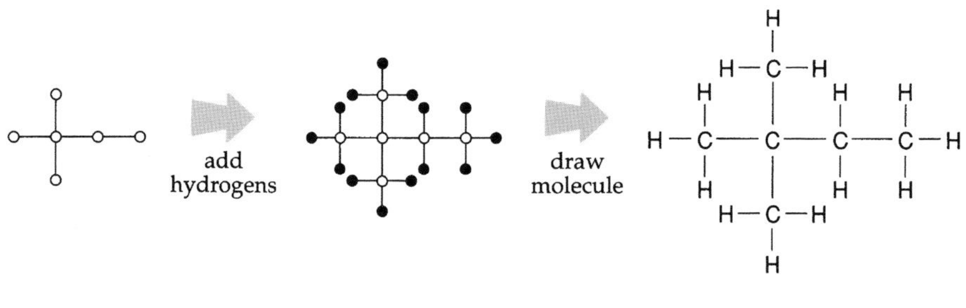

21

Table of alkanes C_nH_{2n+2} for $n \le 5$

n	chemical formula	name	molecule	graph
1	CH_4	methane		
2	C_2H_6	ethane		
3	C_3H_8	propane		
4	C_4H_{10}	n-butane		
		2-methyl propane		
5	C_5H_{12}	n-pentane		
		2-methyl butane		
		2,2-dimethyl propane		

It follows that the problem of counting alkanes is essentially a graph-counting problem. The following table lists the number of different alkanes C_nH_{2n+2} with n carbon atoms, for $n = 1, \ldots , 15$:

n	1	2	3	4	5	6	7	8	9	10	11	12	13	14	15
number of alkanes	1	1	1	2	3	5	9	18	35	75	159	355	802	1858	4347

Problem 1.26 ───────────────

(a) Draw the carbon graph of the molecule

(b) Draw the molecule whose carbon graph is

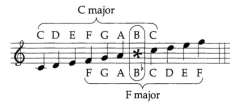

Historical note

Although graph-like diagrams had been used as far back as 1789 to represent molecules, it was not until the 1850s that the way atoms combine was sufficiently well understood for meaningful diagrams to be drawn. This occurred when August Kekulé and others put forward ideas which led to the theory of valency. In 1864 Alexander Crum Brown introduced structural diagrams to represent this theory and explain the nature of isomerism. Meanwhile, the mathematician Arthur Cayley had spent some time studying and counting trees, and in 1875 showed how to calculate the number of alkanes with a given number of carbon atoms.

(c) Music (*optional*)

In a piece of music, certain changes of key sound more natural than others. For example, modulating from the key of C major to the key of F major seems very natural, since only one change of note ($B \rightarrow B^\flat$) is involved:

This case study assumes some knowledge of the theory of music. It is *optional* and will not be assessed.

C major

C D E F G A B C

F G A B♭ C D E F

F major

Two major keys which can be obtained from each other in this way may be said to be *related*, and it seems natural to represent this relationship by a graph whose vertices represent the various keys and whose edges join pairs of related keys. This gives rise to a graph with twelve vertices — the cycle graph C_{12}. Each key is joined to two other keys, called its *dominant* and *subdominant*; for example, C major is joined to G major and F major.

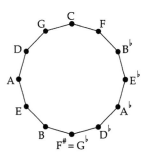

Unfortunately, we run into difficulties when we try to extend this idea to minor keys, since there are many key-changes which sound very natural, but which involve several note-changes. In this case, it is usual to say that each key has *five* closely related keys — its dominant and subdominant, as before, and also the corresponding relative minor keys. For example, the key of C major is closely related to its dominant

We are here assuming 'equal temperament', so that $C^\sharp = D^\flat$, $E^\sharp = F$, and so on.

(G major) and subdominant (F major), and to the relative minors of C major, G major and F major (A minor, E minor and D minor). Joining up these closely related keys leads to the following attractive graph, which has 24 vertices and is regular of degree 5:

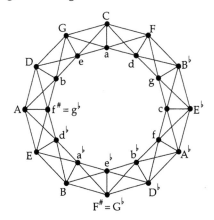

For convenience, we have indicated the minor keys by lower-case letters — for example, e$^\flat$ means E$^\flat$ minor.

Although a knowledge of this graph may not add significantly to your enjoyment of a piece of music, it is nevertheless useful for representing and analysing successions of key-changes. This is because any modulation can be regarded as a combination of the basic key-changes indicated in the above graph. For example, the modulation D$^\flat$ minor → G major can be split up into three constituent key-changes (D$^\flat$ minor → A major, A major → D major, and D major → G major), and is represented in the graph by a path of length 3. In fact, any modulation corresponds to a path in the graph, and we can use the length of the shortest path between any two given keys as an indication of the 'remoteness' of the two keys involved. For example, the modulation C major → F$^\#$ major (path of length 6) is more remote than E$^\flat$ major → A$^\flat$ minor (path of length 4), which in turn is more remote than B$^\flat$ major → C minor (path of length 1). As a general rule, the longer the path in the graph, the stranger the key-change will sound.

The 24-vertex graph above is only one of several graphs which have arisen in a musical context. In fact, graph-like diagrams have been used by several composers, ranging from the baroque era (Bach's 'harmonic circle') to the recent pioneering work of Milton Babbitt, Andrzej Panufnik and others, whose compositions are based, either wholly or in part, on combinatorial considerations.

When Igor Stravinsky was asked how he would describe his music pictorially, he replied: this is *my* music:

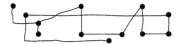

Problem 1.27

Which of the following key changes is the least 'remote'?

(a) A$^\flat$ minor to A$^\flat$ major;

(b) D minor to B$^\flat$ minor;

(c) A major to E$^\flat$ minor;

(d) A$^\flat$ minor to D$^\flat$ major.

(d) Social networks

Graphs have been used extensively in the social sciences to represent *interpersonal relationships*. The vertices correspond to individuals in a group or society, and the edges join pairs of individuals who are related in some way — for instance, x may be joined to y if, for example, x likes, hates, agrees with, avoids, or communicates with y. Such representations have been extended to relationships between groups of individuals, and have proved useful in a number of contexts ranging from kinship relationships in certain primitive tribes to relationships between political parties. Graphs have also been used by political scientists to study international relations, where the vertices correspond to nations or groups of nations, and the edges join pairs of nations that are allied, maintain diplomatic relations, agree on a particular strategy, etc.

We can analyse the possible tension in such situations by using the concept of a **signed graph**. This is a graph with either + or − associated with each edge, indicating a positive relationship (likes, loves, agrees with, communicates with, etc.) or a negative one (dislikes, hates, disagrees with, avoids, etc.). For example, in the signed graph in the margin, Jack likes Jill but not John, Jill likes Jack and Mary but not John, Mary likes John and Jill, and John likes Mary but not Jack or Jill; Jack and Mary have no strong feelings about each other, and are therefore not joined by an edge.

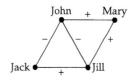

Consider now the following diagrams, which illustrate some of the situations that can occur when three people work together. Which of these situations is most likely to cause tension between John, Jack and Jill?

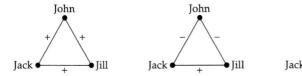

In the first case, all three get on well, and there is no tension. In the second case, Jack and Jill get on well and both dislike John; the result is that John works on his own, and again there is no tension. In the third case, John likes both Jack and Jill and would like to work with them, but Jack and Jill dislike each other and do not wish to work together; in this case, a suitable working arrangement cannot be found, and there is tension. We express this by saying that the first two situations are *balanced*, whereas the third is *unbalanced*.

More generally, we say that a signed graph is **balanced** if we can colour its vertices black or white in such a way that positive edges have ends of the same colour, and negative edges have a black end and a white end. Clearly, the first two of the above diagrams can be coloured in this way, as shown below, whereas the third cannot:

Note that this definition resembles that of a bipartite graph. You can see the connection by taking a balanced signed graph and removing all the positive edges; this leaves a bipartite graph, as indicated by the following diagram:

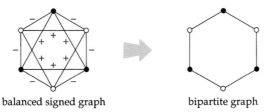

balanced signed graph   bipartite graph

We can exploit this connection between balanced signed graphs and bipartite graphs a little further. Recall from Problem 1.21 that

in any bipartite graph each cycle has an even number of edges.

For balanced signed graphs the corresponding result is that

in any balanced signed graph each cycle has an even number of negative edges.

We ask you to show this in Exercise 1.12(b).

25

Decide which of the following signed graphs are balanced, and find the corresponding bipartite graph for each balanced one:

(a)   (b)   (c)

1.6 Computer activities

The computer activities for this section are described in the *Computer Activities Booklet*.

After studying this section, you should be able to:

- explain the terms *graph, labelled graph, unlabelled graph, vertex, edge, adjacent, incident, multiple edges, loop, simple graph* and *subgraph*;

- determine whether two given graphs are *isomorphic*;

- explain the terms *degree, degree sequence* and *regular graph*, and state and use the *handshaking lemma*;

- explain the terms *walk, trail, path, closed walk, closed trail, cycle, connected, disconnected* and *component*;

- explain what are meant by *complete graphs, null graphs, cycle graphs*, the *Platonic graphs* and the *Petersen graph*;

- explain what are meant by *bipartite graphs, complete bipartite graphs, trees, path graphs* and *cubes*;

- describe the use of graphs in chemistry, the study of social networks and the solution of the four-cubes problem;

- use the graph database to isolate and count simple graphs with a given number of vertices, a given number of edges and a given degree sequence, and to explore the concepts discussed in this section.

2 Eulerian and Hamiltonian graphs

In this section we introduce two important types of graph — Eulerian and Hamiltonian graphs. In particular, we give a necessary and sufficient condition for a connected graph to be Eulerian, and show the connection between Eulerian graphs and diagram-tracing puzzles. We also give sufficient conditions for a connected graph to be Hamiltonian, and show the connection between Hamiltonian graphs and the knight's tour problem and Gray codes. Because of the importance of Eulerian and Hamiltonian graphs in the development of graph theory, some of this section is presented from a historical point of view.

2.1 Exploring and travelling

In this section, we consider two types of problem:

> ## The explorer's problem
>
> An explorer wishes to find a tour that traverses each route between a number of cities only once and returns to the starting point.
>
> ## The traveller's problem
>
> A traveller wishes to find a tour that visits each of a number of cities only once and returns to the starting point.

To appreciate the difference between these two problems, consider the road map shown.

The explorer wishes to find a tour which starts at city a, goes along each road exactly once (in either direction), and ends back at a; two examples of such a tour are

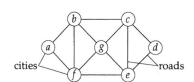

$$abcdefbgcegfa \quad \text{and} \quad afgcdegbcefba.$$

The traveller wishes to find a tour which starts at city a, goes to each city exactly once, and ends back at a; two examples of such a tour are

$$abcdegfa \quad \text{and} \quad afedcgba.$$

Note that the explorer travels along each road just once, but may visit a particular city several times, whereas the traveller visits each city just once, but may omit several of the roads on the way.

Let us regard the road map as a graph whose vertices correspond to the cities and whose edges correspond to the roads. The explorer's problem is now to *find a closed trail that includes every edge of the graph*, whereas the traveller's problem is now to *find a cycle that includes every vertex of the graph*.

With this in mind, we make the following definitions.

> ## Definitions
>
> A connected graph is **Eulerian** if it contains a closed trail that includes every edge; such a trail is an **Eulerian trail**.
>
> A connected graph is **Hamiltonian** if it contains a cycle that includes every vertex; such a cycle is a **Hamiltonian cycle**.

The reasons for these names are given later. You can easily remember which definition is which, since Eulerian graphs are defined in terms of Edges.

For example, consider the following four graphs:

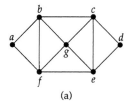 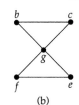 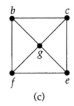 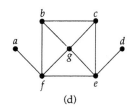

(a)	(b)	(c)	(d)

* graph (a) is both Eulerian and Hamiltonian, as we saw above;

* graph (b) is Eulerian — an Eulerian trail is $bcgfegb$; it is not Hamiltonian;

* graph (c) is Hamiltonian — a Hamiltonian cycle is $bcgefb$; it is not Eulerian;

* graph (d) is neither Eulerian nor Hamiltonian.

Problem 2.1

Decide which of the following graphs are Eulerian and/or Hamiltonian, and write down an Eulerian trail or Hamiltonian cycle where possible:

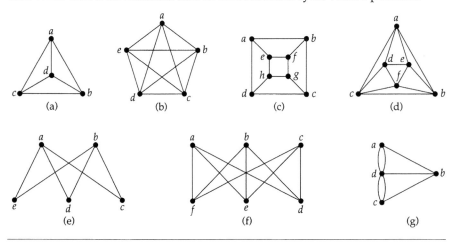

2.2 Eulerian graphs

In the *Introduction* unit, you met the Königsberg bridges problem. In this problem, you are asked to find a route crossing each of the seven bridges of Königsberg exactly once, and returning to the starting point. It was not until Leonhard Euler tackled the problem in the 1730s that it was proved to be impossible.

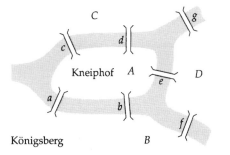

Königsberg

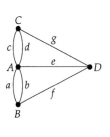

We represented the Königsberg bridges problem in terms of a graph by taking the four land areas as vertices and the seven bridges as edges joining the corresponding pairs of vertices. This gives the graph shown on the right above. The problem of finding a route crossing each bridge exactly once corresponds to that of finding an Eulerian trail in this graph, and you have already seen in Problem 2.1(g) that no such trail exists. It follows that there is no route of the desired kind crossing the seven bridges of Königsberg.

Euler also considered the corresponding problem of finding a route crossing all the bridges in a more general arrangement of bridges and land areas. This led him to present a rule that tells us when such a route is possible, and hence when a graph is Eulerian. In the following problem we ask you to try to formulate this rule.

Problem 2.2

(a) It is clear that finding a route crossing each bridge just once and returning to the starting point (that is, finding an Eulerian trail in the corresponding graph) is possible only when the following condition is satisfied:

> whenever you cross into a part of the city
> you must be able to leave it by another bridge.

What does this tell you about the vertex degrees in an Eulerian graph?

28

(b) Using the result of part (a), guess a rule that tells you whether or not a given connected graph is Eulerian, and test your rule on the graphs of Problem 2.1.

In the solution to Problem 2.2, we gave a rule that tells us whether or not a given connected graph is Eulerian — namely, *check whether all the vertex degrees are even*. We now state this rule formally.

> ## Theorem 2.1
>
> A connected graph is Eulerian if and only if each vertex has even degree.

An explanation of *if and only if* statements and *necessary and sufficient conditions* is given in the Appendix.

This theorem gives a *necessary* and *sufficient* condition for a connected graph to be Eulerian. That is, the statement of Theorem 2.1 is equivalent to the following two statements:

(a) if G is an Eulerian graph, then each vertex of G has even degree.

(b) if each vertex of a connected graph G has even degree, then G is an Eulerian graph.

The proof of Theorem 2.1 is given at the end of this subsection.

Some citizens of Königsberg
Were walking on the strand
Beside the river Pregel
With its seven bridges spanned.

'O Euler, come and walk with us',
Those burghers did beseech.
'We'll roam the seven bridges o'er,
And pass but once by each'.

Problem 2.3

Use Theorem 2.1 to determine which of the following graphs are Eulerian:

(a) the complete graph K_8;

(b) the complete bipartite graph $K_{8,8}$;

(c) the cycle graph C_8;

(d) the dodecahedron graph;

(e) the cube graph Q_8.

'It can't be done', thus Euler cried.
'Here comes the Q. E. D.
Your islands are but vertices
And four have odd degree'.

From Königsberg to König's book
So runs the graphic tale
And still it grows more colorful
In Michigan, and Yale.

BLANCHE DESCARTES
The Expanding Unicurse

Dominoes

An interesting and unusual application of Eulerian graphs is to the game of dominoes. The complete graph K_7 is Eulerian, since each vertex has degree 6. If the vertices are labelled 0, 1, 2, 3, 4, 5 and 6, then an Eulerian trail is obtained by tracing the edges in the following order:

01, 12, 23, 34, 45, 56, 60, 02, 24, 46, 61, 13, 35, 50, 03, 36, 62, 25, 51, 14, 40.

We can regard each of these edges as a domino — for example, the edge 24 corresponds to the domino

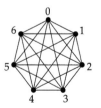

It follows that the above Eulerian trail corresponds to an arrangement of the dominoes of a normal set (other than the doubles 0–0, 1–1, … , 6–6) in a continuous sequence. Once this basic sequence is found, we can then insert the doubles at appropriate places, thereby showing that a complete game of dominoes is possible. The following ring of dominoes corresponds to the above Eulerian trail:

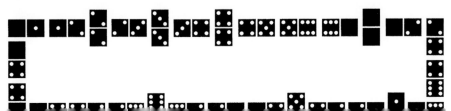

Problem 2.4

By finding an Eulerian trail in K_5, arrange a set of fifteen dominoes (from 0–0 to 4–4) in a ring.

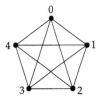

Semi-Eulerian graphs

There are several simple modifications of the above ideas that are worth mentioning. The most important of these arises when we do not insist that the citizens of Königsberg return to their starting point.

> Suppose that the citizens of Königsberg are still keen to cross each of the seven bridges exactly once, but are content to start and finish their walk at different places. Is the walk possible under these less restrictive conditions?

From your work on this problem in the *Introduction* unit, or by a little experimentation with the diagram in the margin, you should be convinced that, even with this modification to the conditions, such a walk is not possible. This leads us to make the following definition.

Definition

A connected graph is **semi-Eulerian** if there is an open trail that includes every edge; such a trail is a **semi-Eulerian trail**.

Recall that an *open trail* is a trail whose ends do not coincide.

Using Theorem 2.1, we can easily give a necessary and sufficient condition for a graph to be semi-Eulerian.

Theorem 2.2

A connected graph is semi-Eulerian if and only if it has exactly two vertices of odd degree.

Proof

Again, there are two statements to prove:

(a) *If G is semi-Eulerian, then G has exactly two vertices of odd degree.*
To see why this is true, we let G be a semi-Eulerian graph, and let v and w be the starting and finishing vertices of an open trail. If we add an edge e joining v and w, we get an Eulerian graph in which, by Theorem 2.1, each vertex must have even degree. If we now recover G by removing the edge e, we see that v and w are the only vertices of odd degree.

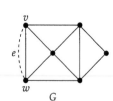

(b) *If G has exactly two vertices of odd degree, then G is semi-Eulerian.*
This is also quite straightforward. For, suppose that the two vertices of odd degree are v and w. If we now add an edge e joining these vertices, we get a connected graph in which each vertex has even degree. By Theorem 2.1, this graph is Eulerian, and so has an Eulerian trail. Removal of the edge e from this trail produces an open trail which includes every edge of G, so G is semi-Eulerian. ∎

It follows from the above discussion that, in a semi-Eulerian graph G, the starting and finishing vertices of an open trail that includes every edge of

Problem 2.5

Use Theorem 2.2 to determine which of the following graphs are semi-Eulerian, and write down a corresponding open trail where possible:

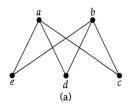
(a)

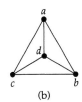
(b)

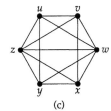
(c)

Problem 2.6

The well-to-do millionaire Count Van Diamond has just been murdered and Hercules Parrot, the internationally known detective and part-time graph-theorist, has been called in to investigate. The butler claims he saw the gardener enter the billiard room (where the murder took place) and then, shortly afterwards, leave that room by the same door. The gardener, however, says that he cannot be the person whom the butler saw, for he entered the house, went through each door exactly once, and then left the house. Hercules Parrot checks the floor plan (given below) and, within a matter of minutes, declares the case solved. Who killed the Count?

the Van Diamond estate

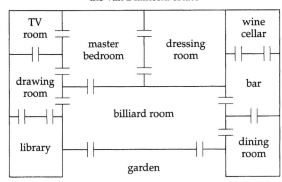

Proof of Theorem 2.1

There are two statements to prove:

(a) *if G is an Eulerian graph, then each vertex of G has even degree;*

(b) *if each vertex of a connected graph G has even degree, then G is an Eulerian graph.*

First we prove part (a). If G is Eulerian, there is an Eulerian trail. Whenever this trail passes through a vertex, there is a contribution of 2 to the degree of that vertex. Since each edge is used just once, the degree of each vertex is a sum of 2s — that is, an even number.

We now prove part (b). We begin by proving that,

> *if each vertex of a graph G has even degree, then G can be split into cycles, no two of which have an edge in common.*

We obtain our first cycle by starting at any vertex u and traversing edges in an arbitrary manner, never repeating **any** edge. Because each vertex has even degree, we know that, whenever **we enter** a vertex, we must be able to leave it. Since there is only a finite number of vertices, we must eventually reach a vertex v that we have already met before. The edges of the trail between the two occurrences of the vertex v must therefore form a cycle, which we call C_1.

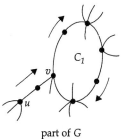

part of G

We now remove from G the edges of C_1. This leaves a graph H (possibly disconnected) in which each vertex has even degree. If H has any edges (that is, if G is not just C_1), we can repeat the procedure above to find a cycle in H, which we call C_2. (Note that C_2 has no edges in common with C_1.) Removing the edges of C_2 from H leaves yet another graph in which each vertex has even degree, and which therefore contains a cycle C_3. We continue in this way until there are no edges left, at which stage we have a number of cycles $C_1, C_2, \ldots, C_k$ that together include every edge of G, and no two of which have any edges in common. This proves the above result.

part of H

We can now complete the proof of part (b).

We have shown that we can split the edges of G into cycles, and we must now fit them together again to make an Eulerian trail. In order to do this, we start at any vertex of the cycle C_1 and travel round C_1 until we meet a vertex of another cycle (C_2, say). We traverse the edges of this cycle, and then resume travelling around C_1, traversing other new cycles as we come to them. This gives us a closed trail that includes C_1 and (unless G is just C_1) at least one other cycle (since G is connected). If this trail includes all the cycles $C_1, C_2, \ldots, C_k$, then we have the required Eulerian trail. If not, we travel round our new closed trail, traversing other cycles as we come to them. (Since G is connected, there will always be at least one cycle to add to our closed trail.) We continue this process until all the cycles have been traversed, at which stage we have the required Eulerian trail. It follows that G is Eulerian. ∎

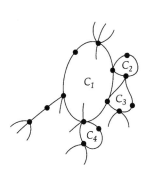

The above proof is not the shortest possible proof; for example, there is a shorter one which uses the method of mathematical induction. However, the advantage of our proof is that it is constructive — it actually shows how to construct an Eulerian trail in a given graph. It also gives us the following result, which is of interest in its own right.

Proofs by mathematical induction are discussed in the Appendix.

Theorem 2.3

An Eulerian graph can be split into cycles, no two of which have an edge in common.

Problem 2.7

Show how the graph on the right can be split into four cycles, no two of which have an edge in common. How can these cycles be combined to form an Eulerian trail?

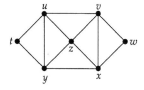

> If you wish, you can now proceed directly to Section 2.4 and read Case study (a), *Diagram-tracing puzzles*.

2.3 Hamiltonian graphs

We now turn our attention to Hamiltonian graphs — graphs in which there is a cycle passing through every vertex.

The name *Hamiltonian* derives from a game invented by Sir William Rowan Hamilton, one of the leading mathematicians of his time. One of his most significant discoveries was the existence of algebraic systems in which the commutative law for multiplication ($xy = yx$) does not hold. His algebra of quaternions, or *icosian calculus* (as he called it), can be expressed in terms of finding Hamiltonian cycles in the graph of the regular dodecahedron, shown below.

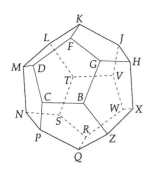
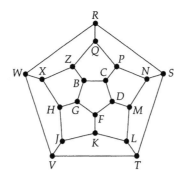

He also turned the problem into a game, the *icosian game*, in which the player has to find Hamiltonian cycles starting with five given initial letters. For example, given the initial letters *BCPNM*, the player can complete a Hamiltonian cycle in exactly two ways:

BCPNMDFKLTSRQZXWVJHGB;

BCPNMDFGHXWVJKLTSRQZB.

The game was marketed in graph form in 1859. It also later appeared in a solid dodecahedron form under the title *A Voyage round the World*, with the vertices representing places — Brussels, Canton, Delhi, ... , Zanzibar.

Hamilton sold the idea of the icosian game to a wholesale dealer of games and puzzles for £25. It turned out to be a bad deal — for the dealer!

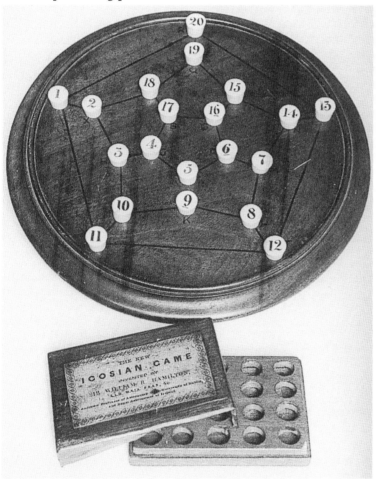

WILLIAM ROWAN HAMILTON (1805–1865)

William Rowan Hamilton was a child prodigy, became Astronomer Royal of Ireland at 22, and was knighted at 30. He did brilliant work in geometrical optics, dynamics and algebra.

Problem 2.8

How many Hamiltonian cycles on the dodecahedron begin with *JVTSR*?

Problem 2.9

Find a path on the dodecahedron starting with *BCD*, ending with *T*, and including each vertex just once.

The name *Hamiltonian cycle* can be regarded as a misnomer, since Hamilton was not the first to look for cycles that pass through every vertex of a graph. An earlier example of a problem which can be expressed in terms of Hamiltonian cycles is the celebrated *knight's tour problem*, which we discuss at the end of this section. Yet another is the *travelling salesman problem*. In this problem, you are given a graph in which the vertices represent locations, and each edge has a *weight*, representing the distance between its endpoints. You are required to find a route that visits each vertex just once, and returns to your starting point, covering the shortest possible total distance. Thus you are required to find a *minimum-weight Hamiltonian cycle* in the graph.

You met this problem in the *Introduction* unit.

Properties of Hamiltonian graphs

At first sight, the problem of deciding whether a given graph is Hamiltonian may seem very similar to that of deciding whether it is Eulerian, and we might expect there to be a simple necessary and sufficient condition for a graph to be Hamiltonian, analogous to that of Theorem 2.1 for Eulerian graphs. However, no such condition is known, and the search for necessary or sufficient conditions for a graph to be Hamiltonian is a major area of study in graph theory today.

Faced with this situation, the best we can do is to look for various classes of graphs that are Hamiltonian. For example, it is clear that the cycle graph C_n is Hamiltonian for all values of n. Note also that the complete graph K_n is Hamiltonian if $n \geq 3$; if the vertices are denoted by $1, 2, \ldots, n$, then a Hamiltonian cycle is $123\ldots n1$.

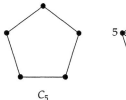

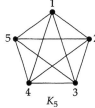

C_5 K_5

Problem 2.10

Which of the following graphs are Hamiltonian?

(a) the complete bipartite graph $K_{4,4}$;

(b) a tree with ten vertices.

Problem 2.11

(a) Prove that a bipartite graph with an odd number of vertices cannot be Hamiltonian.

(b) Use the result of part (a) to show that the following graph is not Hamiltonian:

The graph in part (b) was given as an example of a non-Hamiltonian graph by the Rev. Thomas P. Kirkman shortly before Hamilton became interested in such problems. According to Kirkman, this graph is what we see if we 'cut in two the cell of the bee'.

If we take a Hamiltonian graph and add an edge to it, then we obtain another Hamiltonian graph, since we can take the same Hamiltonian cycle as before. It follows that graphs with large vertex degrees, and hence many edges, are more likely to be Hamiltonian than graphs with small vertex degrees. We can make this idea precise in various ways. One of the most important of these is the following result of Oystein Ore, proved in 1960. We omit the proof.

Theorem 2.4: Ore's theorem

Let G be a simple connected graph with n vertices, where $n \geq 3$. If

$$\deg v + \deg w \geq n,$$

for each pair of non-adjacent vertices v and w, then G is Hamiltonian.

For example, for the graph on the right, $\deg v + \deg w \geq 5$ for each pair of non-adjacent vertices v and w (in fact, for all pairs of vertices v and w), and so this graph is Hamiltonian, by Ore's theorem.

This result is known as *Dirac's theorem*.

Problem 2.12

(a) Use Ore's theorem to show that, if G is a simple connected graph with n vertices, where $n \geq 3$, and if $\deg v \geq n/2$ for each vertex v, then G is Hamiltonian.

(b) Give an example of a Hamiltonian graph that does not satisfy the conditions of Ore's theorem.

Just as for Eulerian graphs, there are several variations of the above ideas and results. For example, we can define *semi-Hamiltonian graphs*, which are graphs where we can visit every vertex but not return to our starting point.

Definition

A connected graph is **semi-Hamiltonian** if there is a path, but not a cycle, that includes every vertex; such a path is called a **semi-Hamiltonian path**.

There is no known general criterion for testing whether a given graph is semi-Hamiltonian.

Problem 2.13

Determine which of the following graphs are semi-Hamiltonian, and give a corresponding path where possible:

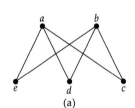
(a)

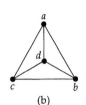
(b)

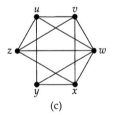
(c)

> If you wish, you can now proceed directly to Section 2.4 and read Case study (b), *The knight's tour problem*, and Case study (c), *Gray codes*.

2.4 Case studies

We conclude this section by introducing three case studies — diagram-tracing puzzles, the knight's tour problem and Gray codes.

(a) Diagram-tracing puzzles

A common type of recreational puzzle is that of drawing a given diagram in as few continuous pen-strokes as possible, without covering any part of the diagram twice. For example, it is easy to draw the diagram on the right with four continuous strokes, but can it be done with three?

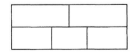

Such problems are equivalent to determining the minimum number of non-overlapping open trails in the corresponding graph.

In 1809 Louis Poinsot, unaware of Euler's solution of the Königsberg bridges problem, showed that diagrams consisting of n points, all interconnected, can be drawn in one continuous stroke if n is odd, but not if n is even:

$n = 3$ yes $n = 4$ no $n = 5$ yes $n = 6$ no $n = 7$  yes

In the terminology of graph theory, this amounts to saying that the complete graph K_n is Eulerian only for odd values of n, since such graphs have even vertex degrees. What is remarkable about Poinsot's account of the subject is that he gave an ingenious construction for finding an Eulerian trail when n is odd — no mean feat, as you will see if you try to describe a method for constructing an Eulerian trail in (say) K_{99}.

In 1847, Johann Listing wrote an important treatise entitled *Vorstudien zur Topologie* (Introductory studies in topology), which included a discussion of diagram-tracing puzzles. In particular, he observed that the diagram on the right has eight vertices of odd degree, and so cannot possibly be drawn with fewer than four continuous strokes. He also remarked that the following diagram can be drawn in one continuous stroke, starting at one end and ending at the other, since these are the only points that correspond to vertices of odd degree:

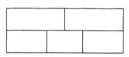

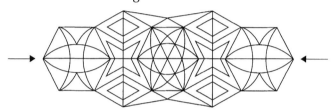

Problem 2.14

How many continuous pen-strokes are needed to draw the diagram on the right?

The following problem answers the question of how many continuous pen-strokes are needed to draw a given graph.

Problem 2.15

Prove that, if a graph has k vertices of odd degree, then the smallest number of continuous pen-strokes needed to cover all the edges is $k/2$.

Hint Add $k/2$ edges, in a suitable manner, to obtain an Eulerian graph.

The number of vertices of odd degree is always even, by the handshaking lemma (see Problem 1.12(a)), so $k/2$ is an integer.

(b) The knight's tour problem

On a chessboard, a knight always moves two squares in a horizontal or vertical direction and one square in a perpendicular direction, as illustrated on the right. A celebrated recreational problem, which has been studied for at least five hundred years, is the following:

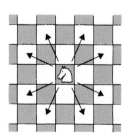

Knight's tour problem

Can a knight visit each square of a chessboard just once by a sequence of knight's moves, and finish on the same square as it began?

In order to see the connection between this problem and that of finding Hamiltonian cycles in a graph, consider the simplified problem of finding a knight's tour on a 4 × 4 chessboard. We can represent the board as a graph in which each vertex corresponds to a square, and edges correspond to those pairs of squares connected by a knight's move. We can deduce that finding a knight's tour is equivalent to finding a Hamiltonian cycle in the associated graph of the chessboard.

In fact, there is no knight's tour on a 4 × 4 chessboard. In order to see this, note that the only way that we can include the top-left square in the tour is to include the two moves shown in figure (a) below. Similarly, the only way that we can include the bottom-right square is to include the two moves shown in figure (b). Combining these, we see that the tour has to include the four moves in figure (c). But these already form a cycle, and so it is impossible to include them as part of a full tour. Thus, no knight's tour is possible on a 4 × 4 chessboard.

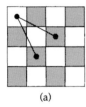 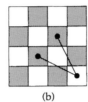 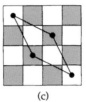

| (a) | (b) | (c) |

There is also no knight's tour on a chessboard with an odd number of squares (such as a 5 × 5 chessboard), as you will see in the following problem. However, for some other chessboards, a knight's tour is possible. The following diagram illustrates a knight's tour on an ordinary 8 × 8 chessboard, thus answering the knight's tour problem in the affirmative.

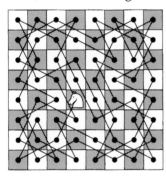

50	11	24	63	14	37	26	35
23	62	51	12	25	34	15	38
10	49	64	21	40	13	36	27
61	22	9	52	33	28	39	16
48	7	60	1	20	41	54	29
59	4	45	8	53	32	17	42
6	47	2	57	44	19	30	55
3	58	5	46	31	56	43	18

This solution is particularly interesting, because if we write down the order of the moves, as in the right-hand diagram, we get a *magic square*, in which the numbers in each row or column have the same total, 260.

Problem 2.16

Show that there is no knight's tour on a 5 × 5 or 7 × 7 chessboard.

Hint Use the fact that a bipartite graph with an odd number of vertices cannot be Hamiltonian.

See Problem 2.11(a).

(c) Gray codes

Engineers sometimes wish to represent the angular position (in multiples of 45°) of a shaft that is rotating continuously. By using an arrangement of brushes on a commutator, which read certain tracks inscribed on the shaft, they convert the angle through which the shaft rotates into a three-bit binary word, as follows:

angle segment	A	B	C	D	E	F	G	H
binary word	000	001	011	010	110	111	101	100

Each three-bit binary word identifies which angle segment is in the position occupied by A in the diagram above.

If we take these binary words as codewords, we obtain a code known as a **Gray code**. As the shaft rotates, *the codeword changes by only one bit at a time as we progress from each codeword to the next in the sequence.* The advantage of such a code is that it minimizes ambiguities that might be caused by misalignments of the brushes that read the tracks.

Gray codes can be found by tracing Hamiltonian cycles on the graph of a cube. For example, the above code and the code

$$000 \to 100 \to 110 \to 010 \to 011 \to 111 \to 101 \to 001 \to 000$$

both correspond to Hamiltonian cycles in the 3-cube, as shown below.

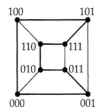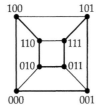

Similarly, to find a Gray code of four-bit binary words, we trace a Hamiltonian cycle in the 4-cube. An example of such a code, illustrated below as a Hamiltonian cycle in the 4-cube, is

$$0000 \to 0001 \to 0011 \to 0010 \to 0110 \to 0111 \to 0101 \to 0100 \to$$
$$1100 \to 1101 \to 1111 \to 1110 \to 1010 \to 1011 \to 1001 \to 1000 \to 0000.$$

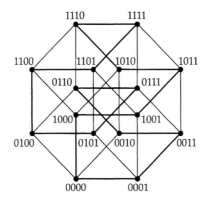

Problem 2.17 ─────────────────────────────

Find another Gray code of four-bit binary words.

───

After studying this section, you should be able to:

- explain the terms *Eulerian graph* and *Eulerian trail*, and state a necessary and sufficient condition for a connected graph to be Eulerian;

- explain the terms *semi-Eulerian graph* and *semi-Eulerian trail*, and state a necessary and sufficient condition for a connected graph to be semi-Eulerian;

- explain the terms *Hamiltonian graph, Hamiltonian cycle, semi-Hamiltonian graph* and *semi-Hamiltonian path*, and state a sufficient condition for a simple connected graph to be Hamiltonian;

- explain the relevance of the above ideas to the Königsberg bridges problem, dominoes, the icosian game, diagram-tracing puzzles, the knight's tour problem and Gray codes.

3 Digraphs

In this section we discuss digraphs and their properties. Our treatment of the subject is very similar to that of Sections 1 and 2 for graphs, except that at each stage we need to take account of the directions of the arcs.

The intuitive idea of a digraph is already familiar to you from the *Introduction* unit.

3.1 Digraphs and subdigraphs

We start by formalizing the definition of a *digraph*.

> ### Definitions
>
> A **digraph** consists of a set of elements called **vertices** and a set of elements called **arcs**. Each arc **joins** two vertices in a specified direction.

For example, the digraph shown has four vertices $\{u, v, w, x\}$ and six arcs $\{1, 2, 3, 4, 5, 6\}$. Arc 1 is directed from x to u, arc 2 is directed from u to w, arcs 3 and 4 are directed from w to v, arc 5 is directed from x to w, and arc 6 joins the vertex x to itself.

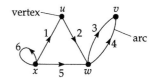

We often denote an arc by specifying its two vertices, in order: for example, arc 1 can be denoted by xu; note that xu is not the same as ux.

Note that the above digraph contains more than one arc from w to v, and an arc joining the vertex x to itself. The following terminology is useful when discussing such digraphs.

> ### Definitions
>
> In a digraph, two or more arcs joining the same pair of vertices in the same direction are **multiple arcs**. An arc joining a vertex to itself is a **loop**.
>
> A digraph with no loops or multiple arcs is a **simple digraph**.

For example, digraph (a) below has multiple arcs and digraph (b) has a loop, so neither is a simple digraph. Digraph (c) has no loops or multiple arcs, and is therefore a simple digraph.

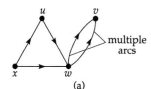
(a)

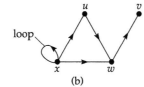
(b)

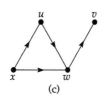
(c)

Problem 3.1

Write down the vertices and arcs of each of the following digraphs. Are these digraphs simple digraphs?

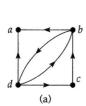
(a)

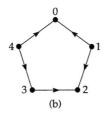
(b)

Problem 3.2

Draw the digraphs whose vertices and arcs are as follows. Are these digraphs simple digraphs?

(a)   vertices: $\{u, v, w, x\}$ arcs: $\{vw, wu, wv, wx, xu\}$

(b)   vertices: $\{1, 2, 3, 4, 5, 6, 7, 8\}$ arcs: $\{12, 22, 23, 34, 35, 67, 68, 78\}$

Adjacency and incidence

We can easily define the digraph analogues of *adjacency* and *incidence*. These are similar to the corresponding definitions for graphs, except that we must take account of the direction of the arcs.

Definitions

The vertices v and w of a digraph are **adjacent** vertices if they are joined (in either direction) by an arc e. An arc e that is directed from v to w is **incident from** v and **incident to** w; v is **incident to** e, and w is **incident from** e.

For example, in the digraph below, vertices u and x are adjacent, vertex w is incident from arcs 2 and 5 and incident to arcs 3 and 4, and arc 6 is incident to (and from) vertex x.

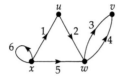

Problem 3.3

Which of the following statements hold for the digraph on the right?

(a)   vertices v and x are adjacent;

(b)   vertex u is incident to arc 2;

(c)   arc 5 is incident from vertex v.

Isomorphism

It follows from the definition that a digraph is completely determined as soon as we know its vertices and arcs, and that two digraphs are *the same* if they have the same vertices and arcs. Once we know the vertices and arcs, we can draw the digraph and, in principle, any picture we draw is as good as any other; the actual way in which the vertices and arcs are drawn is irrelevant.

As you might expect, we can extend the concept of isomorphism to digraphs, as follows.

Definition

Two digraphs C and D are **isomorphic** if D can be obtained by relabelling the vertices of C — that is, if there is a one–one correspondence between the vertices of C and those of D such that the arcs joining each pair of vertices in C agree in both number and direction with the arcs joining the corresponding pair of vertices in D.

For example, the digraphs

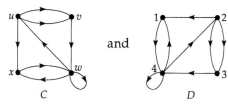

and

are isomorphic, as you can see by considering the one–one correspondence

C: u   v   w   x
    ↕   ↕   ↕   ↕
D: 2   3   4   1

Note that:

the two vertices with loops, w and 4, correspond;

the two arcs from u to v in C correspond to the two arcs from 2 to 3 in D;

the arcs wx and xw in C correspond to the arcs 41 and 14 in D;

and so on.

Problem 3.4

By suitably relabelling the vertices, show that the following digraphs are isomorphic:

Problem 3.5

Are the following two digraphs isomorphic? If so, find a suitable one–one correspondence between the vertices of the first and those of the second; if not, explain why no such one–one correspondence exists.

As with graphs, sometimes it is not necessary to have labels on the digraphs. In such cases, we can omit the labels and refer to the resulting object as an *unlabelled digraph*. For example, the unlabelled digraph

corresponds to any of the following isomorphic digraphs:

We say that two unlabelled digraphs are *isomorphic* if labels can be attached to their vertices so that they become the same digraph.

Problem 3.6

By suitably labelling the vertices, show that the following unlabelled digraphs are isomorphic:

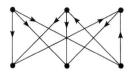

Underlying graphs and subdigraphs

It is convenient at this stage to introduce the idea of the *underlying graph* of a digraph.

Definition

Let D be a digraph. The **underlying graph** of D is the graph obtained by replacing each arc of D by the corresponding undirected edge.

To obtain the underlying graph, we simply remove the arrows from the arcs; for example:

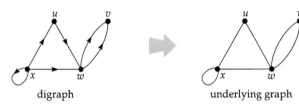

digraph   underlying graph

We can also define a concept analogous to that of a subgraph of a graph.

Definition

A **subdigraph** of a digraph D is a digraph all of whose vertices are vertices of D and all of whose arcs are arcs of D.

Note that D is a subdigraph of D.

For example, if D is the digraph on the left below, with vertices $\{u, v, w, x\}$ and arcs $\{1, 2, 3, 4, 5, 6\}$, then the following are all subdigraphs of D:

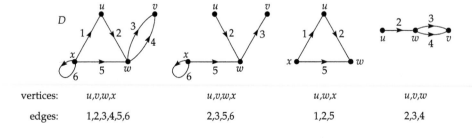

vertices:	u,v,w,x	u,v,w,x	u,w,x	u,v,w
edges:	1,2,3,4,5,6	2,3,5,6	1,2,5	2,3,4

Problem 3.7

Which of the digraphs (a), (b) and (c) are subdigraphs of the digraph D below?

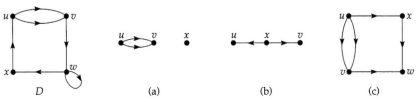

D (a)   (b)   (c)

As with graphs, this definition can be extended to unlabelled digraphs. For example, the following digraphs are all subdigraphs of the unlabelled digraph C:

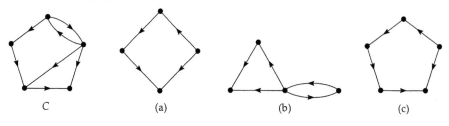

C   (a)   (b)   (c)

Problem 3.8

Which of the digraphs (a), (b) and (c) are subdigraphs of the digraph C below?

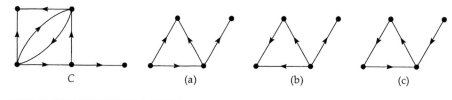

C   (a)   (b)   (c)

If you wish, you can now proceed directly to Section 3.5 and read Case study (a), *Ecology*.

3.2   Vertex degrees in digraphs

We now give the digraph analogues of the degree of a vertex in a graph.

Definitions

In a digraph, the **out-degree** of a vertex v is the number of arcs incident from v, and is denoted by **outdeg v**; the **in-degree** of v is the number of arcs incident to v, and is denoted by **indeg v**.

Each loop contributes 1 to both the in-degree and the out-degree of the corresponding vertex.

For example, the digraph on the right has the following out-degrees and in-degrees:

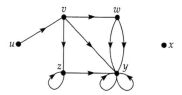

outdeg $u = 1$,   outdeg $v = 3$,   outdeg $w = 2$,
outdeg $x = 0$,   outdeg $y = 2$,   outdeg $z = 2$;

indeg $u = 0$,   indeg $v = 1$,   indeg $w = 1$,
indeg $x = 0$,   indeg $y = 6$,   indeg $z = 2$.

There are also digraph analogues of the degree sequence of a graph, corresponding to the in-degree and out-degree of a vertex.

Definitions

The **out-degree sequence** of a digraph D is the sequence obtained by listing the out-degrees of D in increasing order, with repeats as necessary.

The **in-degree sequence** of D is defined analogously.

For example, the above digraph has out-degree sequence $(0, 1, 2, 2, 2, 3)$ and in-degree sequence $(0, 0, 1, 1, 2, 6)$.

Problem 3.9

Write down the out-degree and in-degree sequences of each of the following digraphs:

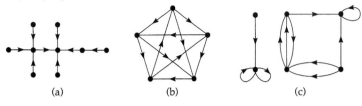

(a)　　　　　　　(b)　　　　　　　(c)

Problem 3.10

For each of the digraphs in Problem 3.9, write down:

　　the number of arcs;

　　the sum of the out-degrees of all the vertices;

　　the sum of the in-degrees of all the vertices.

What is the connection between your answers? Can you explain why this connection arises?

The handshaking dilemma

In the solution to Problem 3.10, you should have noticed that the sum of the out-degrees and the sum of the in-degrees of each digraph are both equal to the number of arcs. A corresponding result holds for all digraphs, and we call it the *handshaking dilemma*!

Theorem 3.1: handshaking dilemma

In any digraph, the sum of all the out-degrees and the sum of all the in-degrees are each equal to the number of arcs.

Proof

Since each arc has two ends, it must contribute exactly 1 to the sum of the out-degrees and exactly 1 to the sum of the in-degrees. The result follows immediately. ∎

3.3　Paths and cycles in digraphs

Just as you may be able to get from one vertex of a graph to another by tracing the edges of a walk, trail or path, so you may be able to get from one vertex of a digraph to another by tracing the arcs of a 'directed' walk, trail or path. This means that you have to follow the directions of the arcs as you go, just as if you were driving around a one-way street system in a town.

We can make this idea precise, as follows.

Definitions

A **walk of length k** in a digraph is a succession of k arcs of the form

　　$uv, vw, wx, \dots , yz.$

We denote this walk by $uvwx\dots yz$, and refer to it as a **walk from u to z**.

A **trail** is a walk in which all the arcs (but not necessarily all the vertices) are different.

A **path** is a trail in which all the vertices are different.

In the digraph in the margin, the walk $vwxyvwyzzu$ is a walk of length 9 from v to u, which includes the arc vw twice and the vertices v, w, y and z twice. The walk $uvwyvz$ is a trail that is not a path (since the vertex v occurs twice), whereas the walk $vwxyz$ has no repeated vertices and is therefore a path.

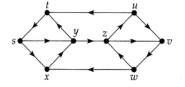

The terms *closed walk, closed trail* and *cycle* also apply to digraphs.

Definitions

A **closed walk** in a digraph is a succession of arcs of the form

$$uv, vw, wx, \dots , yz, zu.$$

A **closed trail** is a closed walk in which all the arcs are different.

A **cycle** is a closed trail in which all the intermediate vertices are different.

In the digraph in the margin above, the closed walk $uvwyvzu$ is a closed trail that is not a cycle (since the vertex v occurs twice), whereas the closed trails zz, wxw, $vwxyv$ and $uvwxyzu$ are all cycles. In describing closed walks, we can allow any vertex to be the starting vertex. For example, the triangle $vwyv$ can also be written as $wyvw$ or $yvwy$.

Problem 3.11 ───────────────────────────────────

For the digraph on the right, write down:

(a) all the paths from t to w;

(b) all the paths from w to t;

(c) a closed trail of length 8 containing t and z;

(d) all the cycles containing both t and w.

As with graphs, we can use the concept of a path to tell us whether or not a digraph is connected. Recall that a graph is connected if it is 'in one piece', and this means that there is a path between each pair of vertices. For digraphs *these two ideas are not the same*, and this leads us to two different definitions of the word *connected* for digraphs.

Definitions

A digraph is **connected** if its underlying graph is a connected graph, and is **disconnected** otherwise.

A digraph is **strongly connected** if there is a path between each pair of vertices.

These three types of connected digraph are illustrated below:

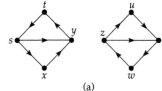
(a)
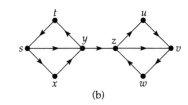
(b)
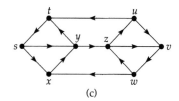
(c)

Digraph (a) is disconnected, since its underlying graph is a disconnected graph. Digraph (b) is connected but is not strongly connected since, for example, there is no path from z to y. Digraph (c) is strongly connected, since there are paths joining all pairs of vertices.

Alternatively, you can think of driving around a one-way street system in a town. If the town is strongly connected, then you can drive from any part of the town to any other, following the directions of the one-way streets as you go; whereas if the town is merely connected, then you can still drive from any part of the town to any other, but you may have to ignore the directions of the one-way streets!

Problem 3.12

Classify each of the following digraphs as disconnected, connected but not strongly connected, or strongly connected:

      (a)   (b)   (c)   (d)

> If you wish, you can now proceed directly to Section 3.5 and read Case study (b), *Social networks*.

3.4 Eulerian and Hamiltonian digraphs

In Section 2, our discussion was concerned with the problem of finding a route that includes every edge or vertex of a graph exactly once, and it is natural to consider the corresponding problem for digraphs. This immediately leads to the following definitions.

> **Definitions**
>
> A connected digraph is **Eulerian** if it contains a closed trail that includes every arc; such a trail is an **Eulerian trail**.
>
> A connected digraph is **Hamiltonian** if it contains a cycle that includes every vertex; such a cycle is a **Hamiltonian cycle**.

For example, consider the following four digraphs:

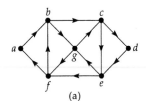   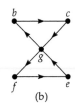   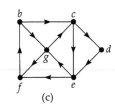   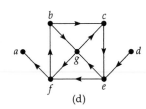

      (a)   (b)   (c)   (d)

- digraph (a) is both Eulerian and Hamiltonian — an Eulerian trail is *abcdefbgcegfa* and a Hamiltonian cycle is *abcdegfa*;

- digraph (b) is Eulerian — an Eulerian trail is *bcgfegb*; it is not Hamiltonian;

- digraph (c) is Hamiltonian — a Hamiltonian cycle is *bcdegfb*; it is not Eulerian;

- digraph (d) is neither Eulerian nor Hamiltonian.

Problem 3.13

Decide which of the following digraphs are Eulerian and/or Hamiltonian, and write down an Eulerian trail or Hamiltonian cycle where possible:

(a)

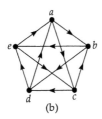
(b)

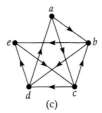
(c)

Much of the earlier discussion of Eulerian and Hamiltonian graphs can be adapted to Eulerian and Hamiltonian digraphs. In particular, there is an analogue of Theorem 2.1. We ask you to discover this analogue in the following problem.

Problem 3.14

(a) Guess a necessary and sufficient condition for a digraph to be Eulerian, involving the in-degree and out-degree of each vertex.

(b) Use the condition obtained in part (a) to determine which of the digraphs in Problem 3.13 are Eulerian, and hence check your answers to Problem 3.13.

We now state the analogues of Theorems 2.1 and 2.3.

Theorem 3.2

A connected digraph is Eulerian if and only if, for each vertex, the out-degree equals the in-degree.

Theorem 3.3

An Eulerian digraph can be split into cycles, no two of which have an arc in common.

The proofs of these theorems are very similar to the proofs of Theorems 2.1 and 2.3, and are left to you to supply if you wish. In the sufficiency part of the proof of Theorem 3.2, the basic idea is to show that the digraph contains a (directed) cycle, and then to build up the required Eulerian trail from cycles step by step, as in the proof of Theorem 2.1.

Similarly, there is a digraph analogue of Ore's theorem, but it is harder to state and prove than its graph analogue, and so we omit it.

If you wish, you can now proceed directly to Section 3.5 and read Case study (c), *The rotating drum problem*, and Case study (d), *Ranking in tournaments*.

3.5   Case studies

We conclude this section by introducing four case studies — ecology, social networks, the rotating drum problem and ranking in tournaments.

(a)   Ecology

Snakes eat frogs, and birds eat spiders; birds and spiders both eat insects; frogs eat snails, spiders and insects. Given any such tangle of interrelationships between predator and prey, how do ecologists sort out the overall predatory behaviour of the various species they are investigating?

When studying relationships between animals and plants and their environment, ecologists use a digraph known as a *food web*. In such a digraph, the vertices correspond to the species under investigation, and there is an arc from a species A to a species B whenever A preys on B.

As an example of a food web, consider the following digraph, which represents the predatory habits of organisms in a Canadian willow forest.

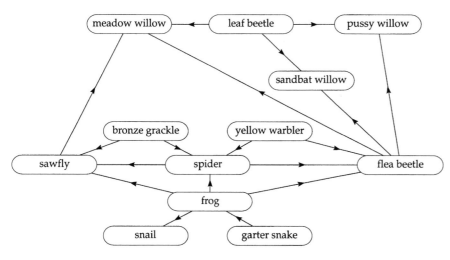

In untangling such food webs, ecologists introduce a graph that tells them which species compete for food. This graph is known as the *competition graph* or *niche overlap graph*, and its edges join pairs of species that share a common prey. For example, in the above food web the bronze grackle and the yellow warbler both eat spiders, and so must be adjacent in the competition graph:

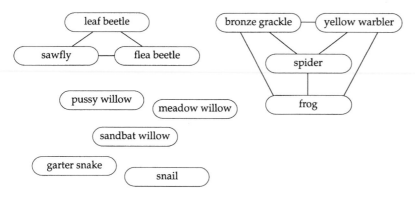

Such a representation has ecological significance in that adjacent vertices

Problem 3.15

Draw the competition graph of the following food web.

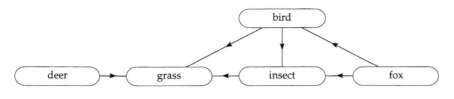

(b) Social networks

In Section 1 we described the use of signed graphs to represent *symmetric* relationships (*x* likes *y* if and only if *y* likes *x*). If the relationships are not all symmetric (*x* likes *y*, but *y* dislikes *x*), we use a *signed digraph*. This is a digraph with either + or − associated with each arc, indicating a positive relationship (likes, supports, threatens, etc.) or a negative one (dislikes, is junior to, is afraid of, etc.). For example, in the signed digraph in the margin, John and Jack like each other, Mary likes Jill but Jill dislikes Mary, John dislikes Jill but we have no information about Jill's feelings for John, and so on.

But signed digraphs also have other uses. Many problems of modern society involve complex systems made up of a number of variables which are constantly changing and interacting. Often we wish to predict the future development of the system when the amount of available information is minimal. For such situations, signed digraphs have proved to be a most convenient form of mathematical model, and their use has led to precise and valid conclusions. In particular, they have successfully been applied to problems of waste disposal, energy planning, research funding, environmental contamination, allocation of medical resources, and so on. Although our discussion here is necessarily simplified, the ideas are also relevant to more complex examples.

Note that a negative arc from *x* to *y* (Jill dislikes Mary) is *not* the same as a positive arc from *y* to *x* (Mary likes Jill).

Positive and negative feedback cycles

The signed digraph below gives a simplified representation of the consequences of changes in energy use. The arc from *p* to *u* is marked positive, since an increase in population in a given area is likely to increase the amount of energy used; whereas the arc from *u* to *r* is marked negative, since the more energy is used, the less it costs per unit. There is no arc from *j* to *r*, since an increase in the number of available jobs has no direct effect on the unit cost of electricity.

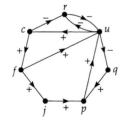

c = energy capacity
f = number of factories
j = number of jobs
p = size of population
q = quality of environment
r = electrical rate (per kilowatt hour)
u = amount of energy used

When following walks through such a signed digraph, we need to be a little careful. For example, the negative sign on the arc from *u* to *q* tells us that an *increase* in the amount of energy used leads to a *decrease* in the quality of environment, and the positive sign on the arc from *q* to *p* tells us that an *increase* in the quality of environment leads to an *increase* in the population. However, if we follow both arcs consecutively, from *u* to *p*, the first tells us that an increase in the amount of energy used leads to a decrease in the quality of environment, as before; but we now need to interpret the second arc differently — the *decrease* in the quality of the environment together with the positive sign on the arc from q to p must be interpreted as leading to a *decrease* in the population. Similarly, following the negative arc from c to r and then the negative arc from r to u must be interpreted as an *increase* in the energy capacity leading to a *decrease* in the electrical rate leading to an *increase* in the amount of electricity used.

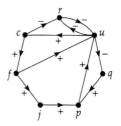

Of particular interest in the above digraph are the cycles. Note that an increase in population (p) results in an increase in the amount of energy used (u), which in turn produces a decrease in the quality of environment (q), which then tends to decrease the population (p). A cycle of this kind, in which an *increase* in any one of the variables (p) ultimately gives rise to a *decrease* in the same variable, is called a **negative feedback cycle**; thus the cycle *puqp* is a negative feedback cycle. On the other hand, an increase in the energy capacity (c) tends to lead to an increase in the number of factories (f), leading to an increase in the amount of energy used (u), thereby increasing the energy capacity still further (c). A cycle of this kind, in which an *increase* in any one of the variables (c) ultimately gives rise to a *further increase* in the same variable, is called a **positive feedback cycle**; thus the cycle *cfuc* is a positive feedback cycle.

c = energy capacity
f = number of factories
j = number of jobs
p = size of population
q = quality of environment
r = electrical rate (per kilowatt hour)
u = amount of energy used

It is easy to see whether a given cycle is a positive or a negative feedback cycle, since *every positive feedback cycle has an even number of negative arcs*, whereas *every negative feedback cycle has an odd number of negative arcs*. The reason for this is that, in a positive feedback cycle, whenever an increase or decrease is counteracted by a negative arc, the counteraction is itself counteracted by the next negative arc. In a negative feedback cycle, there is one counteraction that is never counteracted.

By counting the negative arcs in each cycle, and using the criterion stated above, we see that the cycle *uqpu* is a negative feedback cycle, whereas the cycles *cruc*, *cfuc*, *rur* and *cfjpuc* are all positive feedback cycles. In fact, the existence of several positive feedback cycles containing the vertex c explains why the electrical energy demand system is so unstable, in the sense that initial increases in energy capacity lead eventually to further increases of the same kind. Although this had been observed empirically by environmentalists, the signed digraph representation tells us, from a structural point of view, why it occurs.

Note that, although some of the variables (such as 'quality of environment') may be difficult or impossible to measure, this makes no difference to the conclusions we can draw. Even with such a simple model as this, we can make some remarkably accurate predictions.

Problem 3.16

The following signed digraph is adapted from a study by the Organization for Economic Co-operation and Development into the support that governments should provide for the funding of research projects in science and technology.

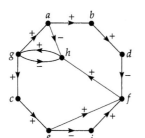

a = number of available jobs
b = number of poorly trained researchers
c = number of well trained researchers
d = amount of 'bad science' produced
e = amount of 'good science' produced
f = public opinion in favour of science
g = amount of available budget
h = pressure to increase budget
i = external or internal threats to society that call for science to alleviate them

List as many positive and negative feedback cycles as you can.

(c) The rotating drum problem

A problem that arises in telecommunications is the *rotating drum problem* or *teleprinter's problem*.

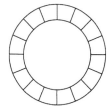 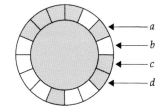

The surface of a rotating drum is divided into sixteen parts, as shown on the left above. We represent the position of the drum by means of four bits — that is, binary digits — a, b, c and d, as indicated on the right above. In this diagram, the shaded areas represent conducting materials and the unshaded areas represent non-conducting materials. Depending on the position of the drum, the terminals represented by a, b, c and d are either earthed or insulated from the earth — for example, in the above diagram, the earthed terminals are a, c and d. The earthed terminals emit a signal represented by 1, and the insulated ones emit a signal represented by 0.

In order that each of the sixteen positions of the drum may be represented *uniquely* by a four-bit binary word $abcd$, the conducting and non-conducting materials must be assigned to the sixteen positions in such a way that all sixteen possible four-bit binary words $abcd$ occur. Can this be done? If so, how can it be arranged?

A solution is given in the right-hand diagram above. The position shown corresponds to the four-bit binary word 1011, where 1 corresponds to a shaded (conducting) area and 0 corresponds to an unshaded (non-conducting) area. Rotating the drum anticlockwise successively gives us the following four-bit binary words:

0110, 1100, 1001, 0010, 0100, 1000, 0000, 0001,

0011, 0111, 1111, 1110, 1101, 1010, 0101, 1011.

These four-bit binary words are all different, and represent all sixteen positions of the drum.

In order to obtain this and other solutions, we construct a digraph as follows:

- there are eight vertices, corresponding to the three-bit binary words

    000, 001, 010, 011, 100, 101, 110, 111;

- there are arcs from each vertex abc to the vertices $bc0$ and $bc1$.

This gives us the following digraph:

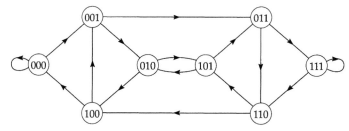

This digraph is clearly Eulerian, since the out-degree and in-degree of each vertex are both equal to 2. Any Eulerian trail can be used to give a solution to the rotating drum problem. For example, if we take the Eulerian trail

$101 \rightarrow 011 \rightarrow 110 \rightarrow 100 \rightarrow 001 \rightarrow 010 \rightarrow 100 \rightarrow 000 \rightarrow$
$000 \rightarrow 001 \rightarrow 011 \rightarrow 111 \rightarrow 111 \rightarrow 110 \rightarrow 101 \rightarrow 010 \rightarrow 101,$

then we can 'compress' consecutive terms cumulatively (for example, the first three terms $101 \rightarrow 011 \rightarrow 110$ compress to 10110) to give the 16-digit sequence

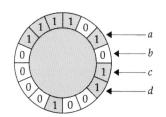

    1011001000011110.

This gives the circular arrangement of positions shown in the margin.

Using a similar argument, we can answer the corresponding question for rotating drums with 32, 64, ... divisions.

Problem 3.17 ———————————————————————————

Find a different Eulerian trail in the above digraph, and hence construct a different solution to the rotating drum problem for sixteen divisions.

(d) Ranking in tournaments

We conclude this section with an application of digraphs that arises in statistics.

A **tournament** is a digraph whose underlying graph is a complete graph — for example, the following diagram shows tournaments with three and four vertices:

    (a)   (b)   (c)   (d)

Such digraphs can be used to record the winners in a round-robin tournament, in which each player plays each of the others. For example:

    in tournament (a), player a beats both players b and c, and player b beats player c;

    in tournament (d), c beats a, b and d, b beats a and d, and a beats d.

Tournaments also arise in other contexts, such as in the *method of paired comparisons*, in which we compare a number of commodities by testing them in pairs. For example, consider the following tournament, used for comparing six types of dog food. These delicacies were tested in pairs on a number of dogs, and the following preferences were recorded:

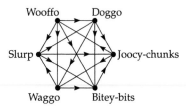

The problem now arises as to how we rank the various commodities in order of preference. For some tournaments there is no difficulty, since we can order them in such a way that each vertex 'beats' the others beneath it; for example, in tournaments (a) and (d) we can rank the participants in this way, as shown on the right.

 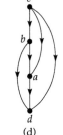

Unfortunately, in many practical examples a direct ranking is impossible; for example, in tournament (b), a beats b, b beats c, and c beats a, so it is not possible to rank these three players directly. There is a similar inconsistency in the dog-food example, where Wooffo was preferred to Doggo, Doggo was preferred to Joocy-chunks, and Joocy-chunks was preferred to Wooffo. For such tournaments we must find alternative methods for ranking the participants or commodities.

    (a)   (d)

In such circumstances, no method is entirely satisfactory, but a method which has been much used in practice is to look for paths containing each vertex — that is, semi-Hamiltonian paths. It can be proved that every tournament has at least one path of this kind, and each such path leads to a ranking.

For example, in tournament (c), possible rankings include *a, b, d, c* and *b, c, a, d*, whereas for the dog-food example, possible rankings include

      Wooffo, Doggo, Joocy-chunks, Waggo, Slurp, Bitey-bits
and
      Bitey-bits, Joocy-chunks, Wooffo, Doggo, Waggo, Slurp.

Once we have listed all the possible rankings of this kind, we then take other considerations into account in deciding which ranking is best for our purposes.

Problem 3.18 ———————————————————————————

How many rankings are possible in the tournament on the right?

After studying this section, you should be able to:

- explain the terms *digraph, labelled digraph, unlabelled digraph, vertex, arc, multiple arcs, loop, simple digraph, underlying graph* and *subdigraph*;

- determine whether two digraphs are *isomorphic*;

- explain the terms *adjacent, incident, in-degree, out-degree, in-degree sequence* and *out-degree sequence* in the context of digraphs, and state and use the *handshaking dilemma*;

- explain the terms *walk, trail, path, closed walk, closed trail, cycle, connected, disconnected* and *strongly connected* in the context of digraphs;

- explain the terms *Eulerian digraph* and *Eulerian trail*, and state a necessary and sufficient condition for a connected digraph to be Eulerian;

- explain the terms *Hamiltonian digraph* and *Hamiltonian cycle*;

- describe the use of digraphs in ecology, social networks, the rotating drum problem, and ranking in tournaments.

4   Matrix representations

Up to now, you have seen two ways of representing a graph or digraph — as a diagram of points joined by lines, and as a set of vertices and a set of edges or arcs. The pictorial representation is very useful in many situations, especially when we want to examine the structure of the graph or digraph as a whole, but its value diminishes as soon as we wish to describe large or complicated graphs and digraphs. For example, if we need to store a large graph in a computer, then a pictorial representation is unsuitable, and some other method is necessary.

One possibility is to store the set of vertices and the set of edges or arcs. This method is often used, especially when the graph or digraph is 'sparse', with many vertices but relatively few edges or arcs. Another method is to take each vertex in turn and list those vertices adjacent to it. By joining each vertex to its neighbours, we can reconstruct the graph or digraph. Yet another method is to give a table indicating which pairs of vertices are adjacent, or indicating which vertices are incident to which edges or arcs.

Each of these methods has its advantages, but the last one is particularly useful. Using this method, we represent each graph or digraph by a rectangular array of numbers, called a *matrix*. Such matrices lend themselves to computational techniques, and are often the most natural way of formulating a problem. There are various types of matrix that we can use to specify a given graph or digraph. Here we describe the simplest — the *adjacency matrix* and the *incidence matrix*.

4.1 Adjacency matrices

Consider the following example:

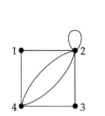

$$
\begin{array}{cccc}
 & \text{col} & \text{col} & \text{col} & \text{col} \\
 & 1 & 2 & 3 & 4 \\
 & \downarrow & \downarrow & \downarrow & \downarrow \\
\text{row 1} \rightarrow & \begin{bmatrix} 0 & 1 & 0 & 1 \\ 1 & 1 & 1 & 2 \\ 0 & 1 & 0 & 1 \\ 1 & 2 & 1 & 0 \end{bmatrix}
\end{array}
$$

On the left we have a graph with *four labelled vertices,* and on the right we have a matrix with *four rows* and *four columns*. The numbers appearing in the matrix refer to the number of edges joining the corresponding vertices in the graph. For example:

A matrix with n rows and m columns is often referred to as an $n \times m$ *matrix*, so that the matrix in our example is a 4×4 matrix.

> vertices 1 and 2 are joined by **1** edge,
> so **1** appears in row 1 column 2, and in row 2 column 1;
>
> vertices 2 and 4 are joined by **2** edges,
> so **2** appears in row 2 column 4, and in row 4 column 2;
>
> vertices 1 and 3 are joined by **0** edges,
> so **0** appears in row 1 column 3, and in row 3 column 1;
>
> vertex 2 is joined to itself by **1** edge,
> so **1** appears in row 2 column 2.

We can generalize this idea, as follows.

Definition

Let G be a graph with n vertices labelled 1, 2, 3, ... , n. The **adjacency matrix** $\mathbf{A}(G)$ of G is the $n \times n$ matrix in which the entry in row i and column j is the number of edges joining the vertices i and j.

Problem 4.1 ————————————————————

Write down the adjacency matrix of each of the following graphs:

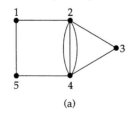
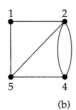

(a)   (b)

Problem 4.2

Draw the graph represented by each of the following adjacency matrices:

$$
\begin{array}{c c}
\begin{array}{c c c c c c}
 & 1 & 2 & 3 & 4 & 5 \\
1 & 0 & 2 & 0 & 1 & 1 \\
2 & 2 & 0 & 0 & 1 & 1 \\
3 & 0 & 0 & 0 & 0 & 0 \\
4 & 1 & 1 & 0 & 0 & 2 \\
5 & 1 & 1 & 0 & 2 & 0
\end{array}
\\
\text{(a)}
\end{array}
\qquad
\begin{array}{c}
\begin{array}{c c c c c c c}
 & 1 & 2 & 3 & 4 & 5 & 6 \\
1 & 0 & 1 & 1 & 1 & 0 & 0 \\
2 & 1 & 0 & 0 & 1 & 0 & 0 \\
3 & 1 & 0 & 0 & 1 & 0 & 0 \\
4 & 1 & 1 & 1 & 0 & 0 & 0 \\
5 & 0 & 0 & 0 & 0 & 0 & 1 \\
6 & 0 & 0 & 0 & 0 & 1 & 0
\end{array}
\\
\text{(b)}
\end{array}
$$

Note that the adjacency matrix of a graph is symmetrical about the *main diagonal* (top left to bottom right). Also, if the graph has no loops, then each entry on the main diagonal is 0, and the sum of the entries in any row or column is the degree of the vertex corresponding to that row or column.

> **If you wish, you can now proceed directly to Section 4.3 and read Case study (a), *Interval graphs*.**

The representation of a graph by an adjacency matrix has a digraph analogue that is frequently used when storing large digraphs in a computer. When defining the adjacency matrix of a digraph, we have to take into account the fact that each arc is *directed*.

Consider the following example:

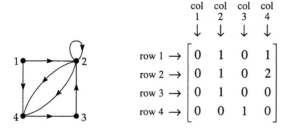

$$
\begin{array}{r c c c c}
 & \overset{\text{col}}{\underset{1}{\downarrow}} & \overset{\text{col}}{\underset{2}{\downarrow}} & \overset{\text{col}}{\underset{3}{\downarrow}} & \overset{\text{col}}{\underset{4}{\downarrow}} \\
\text{row } 1 \rightarrow & 0 & 1 & 0 & 1 \\
\text{row } 2 \rightarrow & 0 & 1 & 0 & 2 \\
\text{row } 3 \rightarrow & 0 & 1 & 0 & 0 \\
\text{row } 4 \rightarrow & 0 & 0 & 1 & 0
\end{array}
$$

On the left we have a digraph with *four labelled vertices,* and on the right we have a matrix with *four rows* and *four columns.* The numbers appearing in the matrix refer to the number of arcs joining the corresponding vertices in the digraph. For example:

vertices 1 and 2 are joined (in that order) by **1** arc,
so **1** appears in row 1 column 2;

vertices 2 and 4 are joined (in that order) by **2** arcs,
so **2** appears in row 2 column 4;

vertices 4 and 1 are joined (in that order) by **0** arcs,
so **0** appears in row 4 column 1;

vertex 2 is joined to itself by **1** arc,
so **1** appears in row 2 column 2.

We can generalize this idea, as follows.

Definition

Let *D* be a digraph with *n* vertices labelled 1, 2, 3, ... , *n*. The **adjacency matrix** **A**(*D*) of *D* is the $n \times n$ matrix in which the entry in row *i* and column *j* is the number of arcs from vertex *i* to vertex *j*.

Problem 4.3

Write down the adjacency matrix of each of the following digraphs:

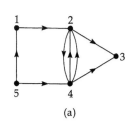

(a)

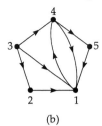

(b)

Problem 4.4

Draw the digraph represented by each of the following adjacency matrices:

$$
\begin{array}{c|ccccc}
 & 1 & 2 & 3 & 4 & 5 \\
\hline
1 & 0 & 1 & 0 & 0 & 1 \\
2 & 1 & 0 & 0 & 1 & 0 \\
3 & 0 & 0 & 0 & 0 & 0 \\
4 & 1 & 0 & 0 & 0 & 0 \\
5 & 0 & 1 & 0 & 2 & 0
\end{array}
$$

(a)

$$
\begin{array}{c|ccccc}
 & 1 & 2 & 3 & 4 & 5 \\
\hline
1 & 0 & 0 & 0 & 0 & 1 \\
2 & 0 & 0 & 0 & 0 & 1 \\
3 & 1 & 0 & 0 & 0 & 1 \\
4 & 1 & 1 & 0 & 0 & 0 \\
5 & 1 & 0 & 0 & 1 & 0
\end{array}
$$

(b)

Note that the adjacency matrix of a digraph is not usually symmetrical about the main diagonal. Also, if the digraph has no loops, then each entry on the main diagonal is 0, the sum of the entries in any row is the out-degree of the vertex corresponding to that row, and the sum of the entries in any column is the in-degree of the vertex corresponding to that column.

> If you wish, you can now proceed directly to Section 4.3 and read Case study (b), *Markov chains*.

4.2 Incidence matrices

For convenience, in this section we restrict our attention to graphs and digraphs without loops.

Whereas the adjacency matrix of a graph involves the adjacency of vertices, the incidence matrix involves the incidence of vertices and edges. To see what is involved, consider the following example:

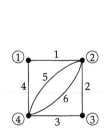

$$
\begin{array}{cccccc}
\text{col} & \text{col} & \text{col} & \text{col} & \text{col} & \text{col} \\
1 & 2 & 3 & 4 & 5 & 6 \\
\downarrow & \downarrow & \downarrow & \downarrow & \downarrow & \downarrow
\end{array}
$$

$$
\begin{array}{l}
\text{row } ① \to \\
\text{row } ② \to \\
\text{row } ③ \to \\
\text{row } ④ \to
\end{array}
\begin{bmatrix}
1 & 0 & 0 & 1 & 0 & 0 \\
1 & 1 & 0 & 0 & 1 & 1 \\
0 & 1 & 1 & 0 & 0 & 0 \\
0 & 0 & 1 & 1 & 1 & 1
\end{bmatrix}
$$

On the left we have a graph with *four labelled vertices* and *six labelled edges*, and on the right we have a matrix with *four rows* and *six columns*. Each of the numbers appearing in the matrix is 1 or 0, depending on whether the corresponding vertex and edge are incident with each other. For example:

vertex ① is incident with edge 4,
so **1** appears in row ① column 4;

vertex ② is not incident with edge 4,
so **0** appears in row ② column 4.

We can generalize this idea, as follows.

56

Definition

Let G be a graph without loops, with n vertices labelled ①, ②, ... , ⓝ and m edges labelled 1, 2, ... , m. The **incidence matrix B(G)** of G is the $n \times m$ matrix in which the entry in row ⓘ and column j is 1 if the vertex ⓘ is incident with the edge j, and 0 otherwise.

Problem 4.5

Write down the incidence matrix of each of the following graphs:

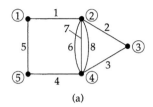

(a)

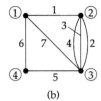

(b)

Problem 4.6

Draw the graph represented by each of the following incidence matrices:

```
    1 2 3 4 5 6 7 8
① [ 1 1 1 1 0 0 0 0 ]
② | 1 1 0 0 1 1 0 0 |
③ | 0 0 0 0 0 0 0 0 |
④ | 0 0 0 1 0 1 1 1 |
⑤ [ 0 0 1 0 1 0 1 1 ]
```

(a)

```
    1 2 3 4 5 6
① [ 1 1 1 0 0 0 ]
② | 1 0 0 1 0 0 |
③ | 0 1 0 0 1 0 |
④ | 0 0 1 0 0 1 |
⑤ [ 0 0 0 1 1 1 ]
```

(b)

In the incidence matrix of a graph without loops, each column contains exactly two 1s, as each edge is incident with just two vertices; the sum of the entries in a row is the degree of the vertex corresponding to that row.

Whereas the adjacency matrix of a digraph involves the adjacency of vertices, the incidence matrix of a digraph involves the incidence of vertices and arcs. Since an arc can be incident from, incident to, or not incident with a vertex, we have to take account of this when defining the matrix. To see what is involved, consider the following example:

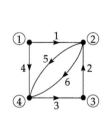

$$
\begin{array}{c}
\text{row ①} \rightarrow \\
\text{row ②} \rightarrow \\
\text{row ③} \rightarrow \\
\text{row ④} \rightarrow
\end{array}
\begin{bmatrix}
1 & 0 & 0 & 1 & 0 & 0 \\
-1 & -1 & 0 & 0 & 1 & 1 \\
0 & 1 & -1 & 0 & 0 & 0 \\
0 & 0 & 1 & -1 & -1 & -1
\end{bmatrix}
$$

col 1   col 2   col 3   col 4   col 5   col 6
↓   ↓   ↓   ↓   ↓   ↓

On the left we have a digraph with *four labelled vertices* and *six labelled arcs*, and on the right we have a matrix with *four rows* and *six columns*. Each of the numbers appearing in the matrix is 1, –1 or 0, depending on whether the corresponding arc is incident from, incident to, or not incident with the corresponding vertex. For example:

arc 4 is incident from vertex ①,
so **1** appears in row ① column 4;

arc 5 is incident to vertex ④,
so **–1** appears in row ④ column 5;

arc 4 is not incident with vertex ②,
so **0** appears in row ② column 4.

We can generalize this idea, as follows.

Definition

Let D be a digraph without loops, with n vertices labelled ①, ②, ... , ⓝ and m arcs labelled 1, 2, ... , m. The **incidence matrix** $\mathbf{B}(D)$ of D is the $n \times m$ matrix in which the entry in row ⓘ and column j is 1 if arc j is incident from vertex ⓘ, –1 if arc j is incident to vertex ⓘ, and 0 otherwise.

Problem 4.7
───

Write down the incidence matrix of each of the following digraphs:

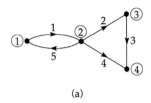

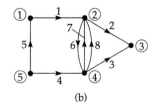

(a)   (b)

Problem 4.8
───

Draw the digraph represented by each of the following incidence matrices:

$$
\begin{array}{c} \\ ① \\ ② \\ ③ \\ ④ \end{array}
\begin{array}{ccccc}
1 & 2 & 3 & 4 & 5 \\
\left[\begin{array}{ccccc}
1 & 1 & 0 & 0 & 0 \\
-1 & 0 & 0 & 1 & 1 \\
0 & 0 & -1 & 0 & -1 \\
0 & -1 & 1 & -1 & 0
\end{array}\right]
\end{array}
$$

(a)

$$
\begin{array}{c} \\ ① \\ ② \\ ③ \\ ④ \\ ⑤ \end{array}
\begin{array}{cccccccc}
1 & 2 & 3 & 4 & 5 & 6 & 7 & 8 \\
\left[\begin{array}{cccccccc}
1 & -1 & 1 & -1 & 0 & 0 & 0 & 0 \\
-1 & 1 & 0 & 0 & -1 & 1 & 0 & 0 \\
0 & 0 & 0 & 0 & 0 & 0 & 0 & 0 \\
0 & 0 & 0 & 1 & 0 & -1 & -1 & -1 \\
0 & 0 & -1 & 0 & 1 & 0 & 1 & 1
\end{array}\right]
\end{array}
$$

(b)

Note that, in the incidence matrix of a digraph without loops, each column has exactly one 1 and exactly one –1, since each arc is incident from one vertex and incident to one vertex; the number of 1s in any row is the out-degree of the vertex corresponding to that row, and the number of –1s in any row is the in-degree of the vertex corresponding to that row.

For reasons of clarity, we have labelled the rows and columns of the adjacency and incidence matrices in Sections 4.1 and 4.2. However, we do not usually bother to do this unless there is a particular need.

4.3   Case studies

We conclude this section by introducing two case studies — interval graphs and Markov chains.

(a)   Interval graphs

Interval graphs have been used extensively in situations involving the arrangement of data into chronological order. In such graphs, the vertices correspond to the objects being arranged and the edges correspond to those pairs of objects that overlap in some way. Although interval graphs first arose in a genetic context, they have also been used in areas such as archaeology. We give a brief account of these applications, indicating how the relevant data can be represented by an interval graph.

Archaeology

At the end of the last century, archaeologists were interested in the various types of pottery and other artifacts that had been found in several graves in predynastic Egypt (c. 4000–2400 BC). In particular, Sir Flinders Petrie and his colleagues used the data from nine hundred graves in the cemeteries of Naqada, Ballas, Abadiyeh and Hu in an attempt to arrange the graves chronologically and assign a time period to each artifact found in them — this process is known as *sequence dating* or *seriation*.

In dating the graves, they assumed that if two different artifacts occurred together in the same grave, then their time periods must have overlapped. They also assumed, since the number of graves was large, that if the time periods of two artifacts overlapped, then the artifacts should appear together in some of the graves.

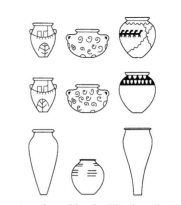

pottery found by Sir Flinders Petrie

One of the most promising approaches to seriation problems in archaeology has been the representation of such data as a graph in which the vertices correspond to the artifacts and the edges correspond to those pairs of artifacts which have appeared together in the same grave. To see how this arises, suppose that there are just six artifacts a, b, c, d, e, f, and that the matrix on the left below tells us which pairs of artifacts occurred together in the same grave; for example, artifacts a and b occurred together in some grave, whereas a and f did not. We can regard such a matrix as the adjacency matrix of a graph, by replacing each ✔ by 1 and each × or – by 0; the adjacency matrix and the corresponding graph are shown below on the right.

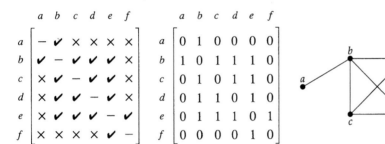

The problem is now to represent this information in chronological form. To do this, we construct a set of intervals on the real line corresponding to the time-periods during which each artifact was in use. Artifacts correspond to intervals, and pairs of artifacts that occurred together in the same grave correspond to overlapping intervals. This means that each vertex of the graph gives rise to an interval and each edge gives rise to overlapping intervals.

One way of doing this is shown below. Note, for example, that the vertices corresponding to artifacts a and b are adjacent, and so their intervals overlap; however, the vertices corresponding to artifacts a and f are not adjacent, and so their intervals do not overlap. Any graph which gives rise to a set of intervals in this way is called an **interval graph**.

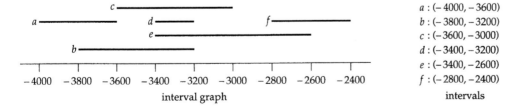

interval graph

$a : (-4000, -3600)$
$b : (-3800, -3200)$
$c : (-3600, -3000)$
$d : (-3400, -3200)$
$e : (-3400, -2600)$
$f : (-2800, -2400)$

intervals

59

Unfortunately, the problem is not as simple in practice as this example may imply. In particular, several different arrangements of intervals may arise from the same graph — for example, we can simply reverse the entire pattern of intervals — and it is usually impossible to choose the correct arrangement unless some other information is available. In spite of this drawback, the interval graph approach has had some spectacular successes, and has led to the solution of many seriation problems, including the chronological ordering of bronze-age material in Central Europe, arrowheads in a palaeo-Indian site in Wyoming, and Greek inscriptions at Histria in Romania.

Genetics

For some time, geneticists have regarded the chromosome as a linear arrangement of genes, and it is natural to ask whether the fine structure inside the gene is also arranged in a linear manner; this problem is called *Benzer's problem*. Unfortunately, this fine structure is too detailed to be observed directly, and so one has to study changes in the structure of the whole gene, known as *mutations*.

In analysing the genetic structure of a particular bacterial virus called phage T4, Seymour Benzer considered the mutations which result when part of the gene is missing. In particular, he studied mutations in which the missing segments overlap, and expressed his results in the form of an *overlap matrix*, part of which is shown as (a) below. This 19 × 19 matrix is the adjacency matrix of the graph (b), in which the vertices correspond to mutations and the edges correspond to pairs of mutations whose missing segments overlap. In these terms, Benzer's problem is that of determining whether the matrix (a) represents the overlapping of a suitably chosen collection of intervals, or (equivalently) of determining whether graph (b) is an interval graph. In (c) we see that this is indeed the case — there *are* intervals which arise from this adjacency matrix and graph. This interval graph is consistent with the parts of the gene corresponding to each mutation being lined up within the gene in a linear fashion in left-to-right order, as shown in (c).

```
structure                                                  A B C C C H
 number   184 215 221 250 347 455 459 506 749 761 782 852 882 103 139 4 33 51 23
 184       0  1  0  1  0  1  0  0  0  0  1  0  0  0  0  0  1  1  1
 215       1  0  0  0  0  0  0  0  0  0  0  0  0  0  0  0  0  0  1
 221       0  0  0  0  1  0  1  1  1  1  1  1  1  1  1  1  1  0  1
 250       1  0  0  0  0  0  0  0  0  0  0  0  0  0  0  0  1  1  1
 347       0  0  1  0  0  0  0  0  0  0  1  0  0  0  0  0  0  0  1
 455       1  0  0  0  0  0  0  0  0  0  0  0  0  0  0  0  0  0  1
 459       0  0  1  0  0  0  0  0  1  1  1  0  0  0  1  0  0  1  1
 506       0  0  1  0  0  0  0  0  0  0  1  0  0  0  0  0  0  0  1
 749       0  0  1  0  0  0  1  0  0  1  1  1  0  0  1  0  0  0  1
 761       0  0  1  0  0  0  1  0  1  0  1  1  0  0  1  0  0  0  1
 782       1  0  1  0  1  0  1  1  1  1  0  1  1  1  1  1  1  0  1
 852       0  0  1  0  0  0  0  1  0  1  1  1  0  0  0  1  0  0  1
 882       0  0  1  0  0  0  0  0  0  1  0  0  0  1  0  0  0  1
 A103      0  0  1  0  0  0  0  0  1  0  0  1  0  0  1  0  0  1
 B139      0  0  1  0  0  0  0  0  0  1  0  0  1  0  0  1  0  0  1
 C4        0  0  1  0  0  0  1  0  1  1  1  1  1  0  0  0  0  1
 C33       1  0  1  1  0  0  0  0  0  1  0  0  0  0  0  0  0  1
 C51       1  0  0  1  0  0  0  0  0  0  0  0  0  0  0  0  0  1
 H23       1  1  1  1  1  1  1  1  1  1  1  1  1  1  1  1  1  1  0
```

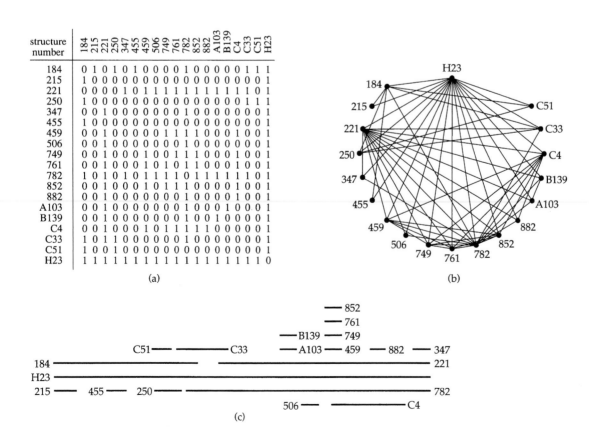

(a)

(b)

(c)

60

Note that, although the representation of this data as an interval graph does not *prove* that the fine structure inside the gene is arranged linearly, it certainly provides support for such a hypothesis. In fact, Benzer extended his analysis to no fewer than 145 mutations and showed that, even with this number of rows, the resulting matrix can still be represented by an interval graph. By this means he was able to show that, for this virus at least, the evidence for a linear arrangement is overwhelming.

Problem 4.9

Draw the graph that gives rise to the following set of intervals:

(1,2), (3,4), (5,6), (7,8), (1,6), (2,7), (3,8).

(b) Markov chains

The study of Markov chains has arisen in a wide variety of areas, ranging from genetics and statistics to computing and sociology. For ease of presentation we consider a rather trivial Markov chain problem, that of the drunkard standing directly between his two favourite pubs, *The Source and Sink* and *The Black Vertex*.

Every minute either he staggers ten metres towards the first pub (with probability $\frac{1}{2}$) or he staggers ten metres towards the second pub (with probability $\frac{1}{3}$) or he stays where he is (with probability $\frac{1}{6}$) — such a procedure is called a one-dimensional **random walk**. We assume that the two pubs are 'absorbing', in the sense that if he arrives at either of them he stays there. Given the distance between the two pubs and his initial position, there are several questions we can ask. For example, which pub is he more likely to reach first? How long is he likely to take getting there?

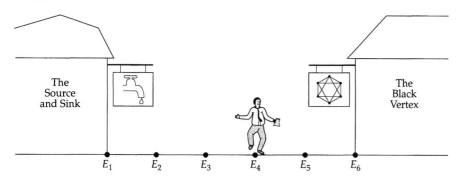

Let us suppose that the two pubs are fifty metres apart and that our friend is initially twenty metres from *The Black Vertex*. If we denote the various places at which he can stop by $E_1, \ldots, E_6$, where E_1 and E_6 denote the two pubs, then his initial position E_4 can be described by the vector $\mathbf{x} = [0, 0, 0, 1, 0, 0]$, in which the ith component is the probability that he is at E_i. Furthermore, the probabilities of his position after one minute are given by the vector $[0, 0, \frac{1}{2}, \frac{1}{6}, \frac{1}{3}, 0]$, and after two minutes by $[0, \frac{1}{4}, \frac{1}{6}, \frac{13}{36}, \frac{1}{9}, \frac{1}{9}]$.

For example, the probability that he is at E_4 after two minutes is given by $(\frac{1}{2} \times \frac{1}{3}) + (\frac{1}{6} \times \frac{1}{6}) + (\frac{1}{3} \times \frac{1}{2}) = \frac{13}{36}$.

It is awkward to calculate *directly* the probability of his being at a given place after k minutes. Fortunately there is a more convenient way of doing this, by introducing the idea of a *transition matrix*.

Let p_{ij} be the probability that he moves from E_i to E_j in any given minute; for example, $p_{23} = \frac{1}{3}$ and $p_{24} = 0$. These probabilities p_{ij} are called the **transition probabilities**, and the 6×6 matrix $\mathbf{P} = [p_{ij}]$ shown is known as the **transition matrix**. Note that each entry of $\mathbf{P}$ is non-negative and that the sum of the entries in any row is 1.

$$\mathbf{P} = \begin{bmatrix} 1 & 0 & 0 & 0 & 0 & 0 \\ \frac{1}{2} & \frac{1}{6} & \frac{1}{3} & 0 & 0 & 0 \\ 0 & \frac{1}{2} & \frac{1}{6} & \frac{1}{3} & 0 & 0 \\ 0 & 0 & \frac{1}{2} & \frac{1}{6} & \frac{1}{3} & 0 \\ 0 & 0 & 0 & \frac{1}{2} & \frac{1}{6} & \frac{1}{3} \\ 0 & 0 & 0 & 0 & 0 & 1 \end{bmatrix}$$

It now follows that if **x** is the initial row vector defined above, then the probabilities of his position after one minute are given by the row vector

$$\mathbf{xP} = [0\ 0\ 0\ 1\ 0\ 0] \begin{bmatrix} 1 & 0 & 0 & 0 & 0 & 0 \\ \frac{1}{2} & \frac{1}{6} & \frac{1}{3} & 0 & 0 & 0 \\ 0 & \frac{1}{2} & \frac{1}{6} & \frac{1}{3} & 0 & 0 \\ 0 & 0 & \frac{1}{2} & \frac{1}{6} & \frac{1}{3} & 0 \\ 0 & 0 & 0 & \frac{1}{2} & \frac{1}{6} & \frac{1}{3} \\ 0 & 0 & 0 & 0 & 0 & 1 \end{bmatrix} = [0\ 0\ \tfrac{1}{2}\ \tfrac{1}{6}\ \tfrac{1}{3}\ 0]$$

and after k minutes by the vector $\mathbf{xP}^k$. In other words, the ith component of $\mathbf{xP}^k$ represents the probability that he is at position E_i after k minutes have elapsed.

In general, we define a **transition matrix** to be a square matrix each of whose rows contains non-negative numbers with sum 1, and a **Markov chain** to consist of an $n \times n$ transition matrix **P** and a $1 \times n$ row vector **x**. The positions E_i are called the **states** of the Markov chain, and our aim is to describe a way of classifying them.

We are mainly concerned with whether we can get from a given state to another state and, if so, how long it takes. For example, in the above problem, the drunkard can get from E_4 to E_1 in three minutes and from E_4 to E_6 in two minutes, but he can never get from E_1 to E_4 because of our assumption that the pubs are 'absorbing'. It follows that our main concern is not with the actual probabilities p_{ij}, but with when they are non-zero. To decide this, we represent the situation by a digraph whose vertices correspond to the states and whose arcs tell us whether we can go from one state to another in any given minute. Thus, if each state E_i is represented by a corresponding vertex v_i, then the required digraph is obtained by joining v_i to v_j if and only if $p_{ij} \neq 0$. We refer to this digraph as the **associated digraph** of the Markov chain. The associated digraph of the above problem is as follows:

Note that the adjacency matrix of the associated digraph of a Markov chain, known as the **associated adjacency matrix** of the Markov chain, is easily obtained from the transition matrix **P** by replacing each non-zero entry of **P** by 1. Thus the associated adjacency matrix for the above problem is as follows:

$$\begin{bmatrix} 1 & 0 & 0 & 0 & 0 & 0 \\ 1 & 1 & 1 & 0 & 0 & 0 \\ 0 & 1 & 1 & 1 & 0 & 0 \\ 0 & 0 & 1 & 1 & 1 & 0 \\ 0 & 0 & 0 & 1 & 1 & 1 \\ 0 & 0 & 0 & 0 & 0 & 1 \end{bmatrix}$$

As a further example, if we are given a Markov chain whose transition matrix is as shown on the left below, then its associated adjacency matrix and digraph are as shown on the right below.

$$\begin{bmatrix} 0 & \frac{1}{4} & \frac{1}{2} & 0 & 0 & \frac{1}{4} \\ 0 & 1 & 0 & 0 & 0 & 0 \\ \frac{1}{2} & \frac{1}{3} & 0 & \frac{1}{12} & 0 & \frac{1}{12} \\ 0 & 0 & 0 & 0 & 1 & 0 \\ 0 & 0 & 0 & 0 & 0 & 1 \\ 0 & 0 & 0 & 1 & 0 & 0 \end{bmatrix} \qquad \begin{bmatrix} 0 & 1 & 1 & 0 & 0 & 1 \\ 0 & 1 & 0 & 0 & 0 & 0 \\ 1 & 1 & 0 & 1 & 0 & 1 \\ 0 & 0 & 0 & 0 & 1 & 0 \\ 0 & 0 & 0 & 0 & 0 & 1 \\ 0 & 0 & 0 & 1 & 0 & 0 \end{bmatrix}$$

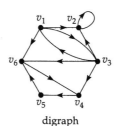

digraph

transition matrix   adjacency matrix

It should now be clear that we can get from a state E_i to a state E_j in a Markov chain if and only if there is a path from v_i to v_j in the associated digraph, and the least possible time to do so is the length of the shortest such path.

A Markov chain in which we can get from any state to any other is called an **irreducible Markov chain**. Clearly a Markov chain is irreducible if and only if its associated digraph is strongly connected. Note that neither of the Markov chains described above is irreducible. For example, in the second Markov chain, there is no path from v_2 to any other vertex.

Problem 4.10 ───

(a) Suppose that, in the problem of the drunkard, *The Black Vertex* ejects him as soon as he gets there. Write down the resulting transition matrix and its associated digraph, and decide whether the resulting Markov chain is irreducible.

(b) How would your answers to part (a) be changed if both pubs eject him?

4.4 Computer activities

The computer activities for this section are described in the *Computer Activities Booklet*.

> After studying this section, you should be able to:
>
> • find the *adjacency matrix* and *incidence matrix* of a given labelled graph or digraph, and find the graph or digraph with a given adjacency or incidence matrix;
>
> • describe the connection between adjacency matrices and problems in archaeology and genetics;
>
> • describe the connection between adjacency matrices and Markov chains.

Appendix: methods of proof

To establish the truth of a mathematical statement, we need to provide a convincing argument, or proof. Our aim here is to explain what such a proof entails, and to describe some methods of proof.

Necessary and sufficient conditions

We start by explaining the connection between *necessary and sufficient conditions* and *if and only if statements*.

Consider the following statement:

IF *G is a tree*, THEN *G is a bipartite graph.*

You were asked to justify this statement in Problem 1.24(a).

This is a TRUE statement, and we say that being a tree is a *sufficient condition* for being a bipartite graph, since it is sufficient for us to know that G is a tree in order to deduce that G is a bipartite graph. However, the *converse* statement

IF *G is a bipartite graph*, THEN *G is a tree,*

which we can write as

G is a bipartite graph, ONLY IF *G is a tree,*

is FALSE, because many bipartite graphs (such as $K_{3,3}$) are not trees. We say that being a tree is not a *necessary condition* for G to be bipartite, since it is not necessary that G be a tree for us to deduce that G is a bipartite graph.

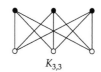

$K_{3,3}$

On the other hand, the statement

IF *every cycle of G has even length*, THEN *G is a bipartite graph*

is a TRUE statement whose *converse*,

IF *G is a bipartite graph*, THEN *every cycle of G has even length,*

which we can write as

G is a bipartite graph, ONLY IF *every cycle of G has even length,*

is also TRUE. Thus having every cycle of even length is a *necessary and sufficient condition* for a graph to be bipartite, for not only is it *sufficient* to know that a graph has cycles only of even length to deduce that it is bipartite, but it is *necessary* that any cycle in a bipartite graph should have even length. We can write

G is a bipartite graph IF AND ONLY IF *every cycle of G has even length.*

Thus, in order to prove a necessary and sufficient condition, that is a result of the form

a is true IF AND ONLY IF *b is true,*

we must prove two separate statements:

You are asked to prove the sufficient condition (the IF part of this statement) in Exercise 1.8 and the necessary condition (the ONLY IF part) in Problem 1.21.

- *a is true* IF *b is true* — that is, we must prove that

  IF *b is true*, THEN *a is true.*

Here, *b is true* is *sufficient* to ensure that *a is true.*

- *a is true* ONLY IF *b is true* — that is, we must prove that

  IF *a is true*, THEN *b is true.*

Here, in order to have *b is true*, it is *necessary* that *a is true.*

In other words, in an IF AND ONLY proof, we have to prove the truth of a statement and its converse.

Methods of proof

To prove a result FALSE, it is enough to produce a single counter-example — for example, consider the following statement:

> IF G *is a bipartite graph,* THEN G *is a tree.*

To prove that this statement is FALSE, it is sufficient to cite the counter-example $K_{3,3}$.

However, to prove a result TRUE, we must produce a general argument which covers all possibilities. The three types of proof which appear most in this course are *direct proofs, indirect proofs* (proofs by contradiction), and *proofs by mathematical induction*. We look at each of these in turn.

Direct proofs

In a direct proof (the most common type of proof), we start with the information we are given and proceed by logical steps to the result required. An example of such a proof is the proof we gave for Theorem 1.2.

Theorem 1.2

Let G be an r-regular graph with n vertices; then G has exactly $nr/2$ edges.

Proof

There are n vertices each of degree r, so the sum of the degrees of all the vertices is nr. By the handshaking lemma, the number of edges is one-half of this amount, which is $nr/2$. ∎

Indirect proofs

These proofs are often called *proofs by contradiction* or *proofs by the method of 'reductio ad absurdum'.* In order to prove indirectly a statement of the form

> IF a *is true,* THEN b *is true,*

we prove that

> IF a *is true* AND b *is false,* THEN a *must also be false,*

thereby obtaining a contradiction. An example of such a proof is the proof we gave for the following statement.

In any graph, the number of vertices of odd degree is even.

We asked you to prove this statement in Problem 1.12(a).

Proof

For any graph, the handshaking lemma holds, so that the sum of the vertex degrees is twice the number of edges, and is thus an even number. If the number of vertices of odd degree were odd, then the sum of the vertex degrees would be an odd number, giving a contradiction. So the number of vertices of odd degree must be even. ∎

Proofs by mathematical induction

Suppose that we wish to prove a statement concerning a particular type of graph with a given number of vertices — for example,

> *the complete graph K_n has exactly $n(n-1)/2$ edges*

See page 14.

or

> *every tree with n vertices has exactly $n-1$ edges.*

See Problem 1.24(b).

One approach to proving statements of this kind is to use the *principle of mathematical induction*, in the following way.

STEP 1   Show that the result holds for appropriate graphs with one vertex.

STEP 2   Show that, for each integer $n > 1$, if the result holds for appropriate graphs with fewer than n vertices, then it must also hold for appropriate graphs with exactly n vertices.

We can thus deduce successively that:

> since the statement holds for graphs with fewer than two vertices (Step 1), it must hold for graphs with two vertices (Step 2);

> since the statement holds for graphs with fewer than three vertices (shown above), it must hold for graphs with three vertices (Step 2);

> since the statement holds for graphs with fewer than four vertices (shown above), it must hold for graphs with four vertices (Step 2);

and so on. We can thus deduce, by the *principle of mathematical induction*, that the result must hold for graphs with *any* given number of vertices, n.

This method is sometimes called the *method of strong induction*. We illustrate it by proving the two statements above.

Theorem A.1

The complete graph K_n has exactly $n(n-1)/2$ edges.

Proof

STEP 1   The result holds when $n = 1$, since K_1 has 0 edges and $(1 \times 0)/2 = 0$.

STEP 2   We now assume that the result holds for complete graphs with fewer than n vertices — that is, that K_k has $k(k-1)/2$ edges whenever $k < n$. We must deduce that K_n has $n(n-1)/2$ edges.

To do this, we remove any vertex v of K_n, together with its $n-1$ incident edges. The remaining graph is the complete graph K_{n-1}, which, by our assumption, has $(n-1)(n-2)/2$ edges. Reinstating the vertex v gives, for K_n, a total of

$$(n-1)(n-2)/2 + (n-1) = [(n-2)/2 + 1](n-1) = n(n-1)/2$$

edges. Thus, if the result holds for complete graphs with fewer than n vertices, then it holds for the one with n vertices.

Therefore, by the principle of mathematical induction, the result is true for all n. ∎

Theorem A.2

Every tree with n vertices has exactly $n-1$ edges.

Proof

STEP 1   The result holds when $n = 1$, since the only tree with one vertex is K_1, which has no edges.

STEP 2   We now assume that the result holds for trees with fewer than n vertices — that is, that every tree with k vertices has $k-1$ edges whenever $k < n$. We must deduce that every tree T with n vertices has $n-1$ edges.

To do this, we remove any edge e of T. Since T has no cycles, this disconnects T and gives two trees, with k_1 and k_2 vertices, say, where $k_1 + k_2 = n$. By our assumption, these trees have $k_1 - 1$ and $k_2 - 1$ edges, respectively. Reinstating the edge e gives, for T, a total of

$$(k_1 - 1) + (k_2 - 1) + 1 = k_1 + k_2 - 1 = n - 1$$

edges. Thus, if the result holds for trees with fewer than n vertices, then it holds for those with n vertices.

Therefore, by the principle of mathematical induction, the result is true for all n. ∎

A similar induction approach can be used when we wish to prove statements concerning particular types of graph with a given number of *edges* rather than a given number of vertices. For example, we can adapt the proof of Theorem A.2 to show that every tree with m edges has exactly $m + 1$ vertices. In such proofs, we usually replace the words 'with one vertex' in Step 1 by 'with no edges', rather than by 'with one edge'.

> ## Theorem A.3
>
> Every tree with m edges has exactly $m + 1$ vertices.

Proof

STEP 1   The result holds when $m = 0$, since the only tree with no edges is K_1, which has one vertex.

STEP 2   We now assume that the result holds for trees with fewer than m edges — that is, that every tree with k edges has $k + 1$ vertices whenever $k < m$. We must deduce that every tree T with m edges has $m + 1$ vertices.

To do this, we remove any edge e of T. Since T has no cycles, this disconnects T and gives two trees, with k_1 and k_2 edges, say, where $k_1 + k_2 = m - 1$. By our assumption, these trees have $k_1 + 1$ and $k_2 + 1$ vertices, respectively. Reinstating the edge e gives, for T, a total of

$$(k_1 + 1) + (k_2 + 1) = k_1 + k_2 + 2 = m + 1$$

vertices. Thus, if the result holds for trees with fewer than m edges, then it holds for those with m edges.

Therefore, by the principle of mathematical induction, the result is true for all m. ∎

In this course, you will see both types of induction proof: those involving induction on the number of vertices and those involving induction on the number of edges.

If removing e did not disconnect T, then the two vertices joined by e must still be connected, by a unique path, and this path together with e would form a cycle — a contradiction.

Further reading

The material in this unit is covered in most books on graph theory — for example:

G. Chartrand and L. Lesniak, *Graphs and Digraphs,* 2nd edition, Wadsworth & Brooks/Cole, 1986.

G. Chartrand and O. R. Oellermann, *Applied and Algorithmic Graph Theory*, McGraw–Hill, 1993.

J. Clark and D. A. Holton, *A First Look at Graph Theory*, World Scientific Publishing, 1991.

J. A. Bondy and U. S. R. Murty, *Graph Theory with Applications,* American Elsevier, 1979.

R. J. Wilson, *Introduction to Graph Theory*, 3rd edition, Longman, 1985.

The applications of graphs and digraphs are more scattered in the literature. A good overall account of several applications may be found in:

M. N. Swamy and K. Thulasiraman, *Graphs, Networks and Algorithms,* Wiley, 1981.

R. J. Wilson and L. W. Beineke (eds), *Applications of Graph Theory,* Academic Press, 1979.

Social networks and interval graphs are covered in:

F. Roberts, *Discrete Mathematical Models, with Applications to Social, Biological and Environmental Problems,* Prentice–Hall, 1976.

Further references to particular topics are given in the above books.

Acknowledgements

p.15 picture of Petersen, courtesy of the Mittag–Leffler Institute, Djursholm, Sweden;

p.28 picture of Euler, courtesy of the Royal College of Physicians;

p.29 The Expanding Unicurse by B. Descartes, courtesy of Professor W. T. Tutte, University of Waterloo, Waterloo, Ontario, Canada;

p.31 Problem 2.6, modified from pages 64–65 of *Graphs as Mathematical Models* by G. Chartrand, courtesy of the publishers Prindle, Weber & Schmidt Inc., Boston, Massachusetts, USA;

p.33 picture of Hamilton, courtesy of the Mary Evans Picture Library;

p.33 picture of the Icosian Game, courtesy of the Royal Irish Academy.

Exercises

Section 1

1.1 Consider the graph G on the right:

(a) Which of the following statements hold for G?

    (1) vertices v and x are adjacent;

    (2) edge 6 is incident with vertex w;

    (3) vertex x is incident with edge 4.

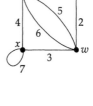

(b) Verify that the handshaking lemma holds for G.

(c) Write down:

    (1) a walk of length 7 between u and w;

    (2) all the cycles of lengths 1, 2, 3 and 4;

    (3) a path of maximum length.

1.2 By suitably labelling the vertices, show that the following graphs are isomorphic:

1.3

(a) If two graphs have the same degree sequence, must they be isomorphic?

(b) If two graphs are isomorphic, must they have the same degree sequence?

1.4 Let G be a graph with degree sequence $(1, 2, 3, 4)$. Write down the number of vertices and edges of G, and construct such a graph.
Are there any *simple* graphs with degree sequence $(1, 2, 3, 4)$?

1.5 Prove that, if G is a simple graph with at least two vertices, then G has two or more vertices of the same degree.

1.6 How many edges has each of the following graphs?

    (a) C_{10};   (b) $K_{9,10}$;   (c) K_{10};   (d) Q_5;

    (e) the dodecahedron.

1.7 The **complement** of a simple graph G is obtained by taking the vertices of G and joining two of them whenever they are *not* joined in G.

(a) Verify that the complement of P_4 is P_4;

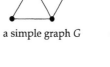

a simple graph G complement of G

(b) What is the complement of K_4? of $K_{3,3}$? of C_5?

(c) Show that, if a simple graph G is isomorphic to its complement, then the number of vertices of G has the form $4k$ or $4k + 1$, for some positive integer k.

(d) Find all the simple graphs with four or five vertices that are isomorphic to their complements.

1.8 Prove that, if every cycle of a graph G has even length, then G is bipartite.

Hint Consider a connected graph G. Choose a vertex v in G and consider those vertices whose minimum distance from v is an odd number and those whose minimum distance from v is an even number. To which vertices are the 'odd' vertices adjacent? To which are the 'even' ones adjacent?

The *minimum distance* between two vertices is the length of the shortest path between them.

Case studies

1.9 Four-cubes problem

Show that the subgraphs H_1 and H_2 of the graph G shown below are the *only* pair of subgraphs satisfying the following properties for the given set of cubes:

(a) each contains exactly one edge from the graph for each cube;

(b) they have no edges in common;

(c) each vertex is incident with two edges.

Hint First show that neither subgraph can contain the loop at R, then repeat the process for the loop at G and then for the edge joining R and Y.

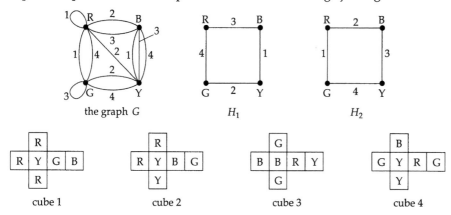

the graph G H_1 H_2

	R		
R	Y	G	B
	R		

cube 1

	R		
R	Y	B	G
	Y		

cube 2

	G		
B	B	R	Y
	G		

cube 3

	B		
G	Y	R	G
	Y		

cube 4

1.10 Chemistry

Write down the numbers of vertices and edges in the graphs of molecules with the formulas C_3H_8, C_4H_{10} and C_5H_{12}. Comment on your results.

1.11 Music

Which of the following key-changes is the least 'remote'?

(a) D major to $E^\flat$ minor;

(b) $B^\flat$ minor to F major;

(c) $F^\#$ minor to $F^\#$ major;

(d) $E^\flat$ major to $D^\flat$ minor.

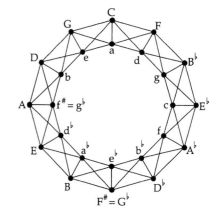

1.12 Social networks

(a) John likes Joan, Jean and Jane, but dislikes both Joe and Jill; Jill and Joe like each other, but both dislike John, Joan, Jean and Jane; Joan, Jean and Jane like each other and John, but each dislikes Joe and Jill. Draw the signed graph representing these relationships, and determine whether it is balanced.

(b) Prove that, in any balanced signed graph, any cycle has an even number of negative edges.

Section 2

2.1 For which values of n, r and s are the following graphs Eulerian? For which values are they semi-Eulerian?

(a) the complete graph K_n;

(b) the complete bipartite graph $K_{r,s}$;

(c) the cycle graph C_n;

(d) the n-cube Q_n.

2.2 Write down all the ways in which the following Eulerian graph can be split into cycles, no two of which have any edges in common.

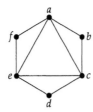

2.3 Theorems 2.1 and 2.2 tell us about the properties of connected graphs with zero or two vertices of odd degree. What can you say about connected graphs with exactly one vertex of odd degree?

2.4 For which values of n, r and s are the graphs in Exercise 2.1 Hamiltonian? For which values are they semi-Hamiltonian?

2.5 Check whether the conditions of Ore's theorem hold for the following Hamiltonian graphs:

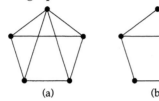

(a)   (b)

2.6

(a) Let G be a simple connected graph with n vertices and $(n-1)(n-2)/2 + 2$ edges. Use Ore's theorem to prove that G is Hamiltonian.

(b) Give an example of a non-Hamiltonian simple connected graph with n vertices and $(n-1)(n-2)/2 + 1$ edges.

Case studies

2.7 Diagram-tracing puzzles

How many continuous pen-strokes are needed to draw each of the following diagrams without covering any part twice?

(a)   (b)

2.8 Knight's tour problem

Prove that there is no knight's tour on a 3×6 chessboard.

Section 3

3.1 Consider the digraph D on the right:

(a) Which of the following statements hold for D?

    (1) vertices u and x are adjacent;

    (2) arc 2 is incident to vertex w;

    (3) vertex x is incident from arc 3.

(b) Verify that the handshaking dilemma holds for D.

(c) Write down (if possible):

    (1) a walk of length 7 from u to w;

    (2) cycles of lengths 1, 2, 3 and 4;

    (3) a path of maximum length.

3.2 Of the following four digraphs, which two are the same, which one is isomorphic to these two, and which is not isomorphic to any of the others?

(a)

(b)

(c)

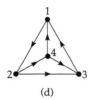
(d)

3.3 A graph is **orientable** if a direction can be assigned to each edge in such a way that the resulting digraph is strongly connected. Show that K_5 and the Petersen graph are orientable, and find a graph that is not.

K_5

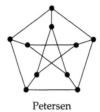
Petersen

3.4 Are the following digraphs Eulerian? Hamiltonian?

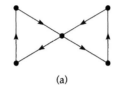
(a)

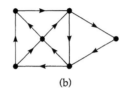
(b)

3.5 In the digraph on the right, find:

(a) all cycles of lengths 3, 4 and 5;

(b) an Eulerian trail;

(c) a Hamiltonian cycle.

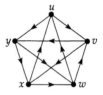

Case studies

3.6 *Social networks*

The following signed digraph was used in a transport study in Vancouver to determine whether a large increase in the funding of public transport would make city travelling easier:

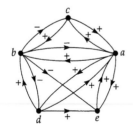

a = cost of an automobile

b = amount of automobile use

c = convenience of automobile use

d = freedom of choice in travel time

e = speed

Determine whether each of the following cycles is a positive or a negative feedback cycle:

(a) *abca*; (b) *beacb*; (c) *adea*.

3.7 *Ranking in tournaments*

Draw all the tournaments with four vertices.
In which of them can the participants be ranked in just one way?

Section 4

4.1 Write down the adjacency matrices of the following graph and digraph:

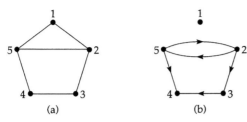

         (a)   (b)

4.2 Write down the incidence matrices of the following graph and digraph:

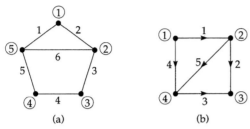

         (a)   (b)

4.3 Write down the graph corresponding to adjacency matrix (a) and the digraph corresponding to adjacency matrix (b).

$$\begin{bmatrix} 0 & 1 & 1 & 1 & 0 \\ 1 & 0 & 0 & 0 & 1 \\ 1 & 0 & 0 & 0 & 1 \\ 1 & 0 & 0 & 0 & 1 \\ 0 & 1 & 1 & 1 & 0 \end{bmatrix} \qquad \begin{bmatrix} 0 & 1 & 0 & 0 & 1 \\ 1 & 0 & 0 & 1 & 0 \\ 0 & 0 & 0 & 0 & 0 \\ 1 & 0 & 1 & 0 & 0 \\ 0 & 1 & 0 & 2 & 0 \end{bmatrix}$$

         (a)   (b)

4.4 Draw the digraph whose incidence matrix is:

$$\begin{bmatrix} 1 & -1 & 1 & -1 & 0 & 0 & 0 & 0 \\ -1 & 1 & 0 & 0 & -1 & 1 & 0 & 0 \\ 0 & 0 & 0 & 0 & 0 & 0 & 0 & 0 \\ 0 & 0 & 0 & 1 & 0 & -1 & -1 & -1 \\ 0 & 0 & -1 & 0 & 1 & 0 & 1 & 1 \end{bmatrix}$$

Case studies

4.5 *Interval graphs*

Show that the cycle graph C_4 is not an interval graph.

4.6 *Markov chains*

The transition matrix of a Markov chain is as follows:

$$\begin{bmatrix} 0 & 0.5 & 0.3 & 0 & 0.2 \\ 1 & 0 & 0 & 0 & 0 \\ 0.5 & 0.5 & 0 & 0 & 0 \\ 0.4 & 0.4 & 0 & 0 & 0.2 \\ 0 & 0 & 0 & 0.1 & 0.9 \end{bmatrix}$$

Draw the associated adjacency matrix and digraph. Is the Markov chain irreducible?

Solutions to the exercises

1.1

(a) (1) is false; (2) and (3) are true.

(b) deg $u = 4$, deg $v = 2$, deg $w = 4$, deg $x = 4$, and so the sum of the vertex degrees is 14. There are seven edges, and so the sum of the vertex degrees is twice the number of edges, as required.

(c) (1) There are various possibilities — for example, the walk with edges 1, 2, 3, 4, 5, 6, 5;

(2) length 1: the loop 7;

length 2: the multiple edges 5 and 6;

length 3: the triangles with edges 1, 2, 5; 1, 2, 6; 3, 4, 5; 3, 4, 6;

length 4: the quadrilateral with edges 1, 2, 3, 4.

(3) As there are only four vertices, no path can have length greater than 3; a path of length 3 is $uvwx$, with edges 1, 2, 3; there are several other possibilities.

1.2 One possible labelling is as follows:

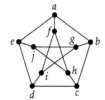 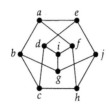

1.3

(a) No — for example, the following non-isomorphic graphs both have degree sequence (1, 2, 2, 2, 3):

(b) Yes.

1.4 Any graph with this degree sequence has 4 vertices and, by the handshaking lemma, $(1 + 2 + 3 + 4)/2 = 5$ edges. An example of such a graph is shown in the margin.

There cannot be a simple graph with this degree sequence, since the vertex of degree 4 would need to be adjacent to four other vertices, which is impossible, as there are only *three* other vertices.

1.5 If $n \geq 2$ and G has n vertices, no two of which have the same degree, then the vertex degrees must be 0, 1, 2, ... , $n - 2$ and $n - 1$. Since the vertex of degree $n - 1$ must be adjacent to each of the other vertices, it must in particular be adjacent to the vertex of degree 0, which is impossible. This contradiction establishes the result.

1.6 (a) 10; (b) 90; (c) 45; (d) 80; (e) 30.

1.7

(a) The following diagram shows P_4 and its complement:

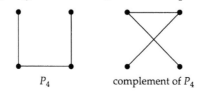

P_4 complement of P_4

Clearly, the latter is isomorphic to P_4

(b)   The complements are as follows:

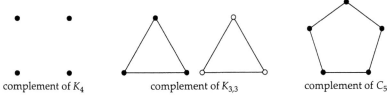

complement of K_4 complement of $K_{3,3}$ complement of C_5

(c)   If the simple graph G with n vertices is isomorphic to its complement, then G must have exactly half the total possible number of edges — that is, $n(n-1)/4$ edges. This number is an integer only when $n = 4k$ or $4k + 1$, for some positive integer k.

The total possible number of edges in a simple graph with n vertices is the number of edges in the complete graph with n vertices, namely $n(n-1)/2$.

(d)   There are three such graphs — P_4, C_5 and the following graph:

1.8   It is sufficient to prove the result for a connected graph, because if the graph is disconnected we can consider one component at a time.

Let G be a connected graph in which each cycle has even length. Choose any vertex v in G. Divide the vertices of G into two sets as follows:

  A is the set of vertices such that the shortest path from each vertex in A to v is of odd length;

  B is the set of vertices such that the shortest path from each vertex in B to v is of even length.

Then v is in B, and the sets A and B have no vertices in common.

Further, no two vertices a_1 and a_2 in A are adjacent, because if they were there would be a cycle $v...a_1a_2...v$ of odd length in G. Similarly, no two vertices b_1 and b_2 in B are adjacent, because if they were there would be a cycle $v...b_1b_2...v$ of odd length in G.

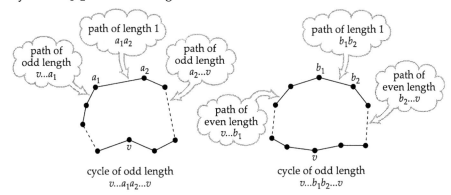

cycle of odd length
$v...a_1a_2...v$

cycle of odd length
$v...b_1b_2...v$

It follows that each edge in G joins a vertex in A to a vertex in B, and so G is bipartite.

1.9   If one of the subgraphs, H_1 say, contains the loop at R, then it cannot contain any other edge incident with R, by property (c). It follows from property (a) that H_1 must contain the 2-edge GY and one of the 4-edges incident with Y. It now follows, by properties (a) and (c), that H_1 must contain the 3-edge BY. Hence Y is incident with three edges, contradicting property (c). Thus, neither subgraph can contain the loop at R.

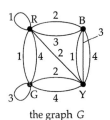

the graph G

Similarly, neither subgraph can contain the loop at G.

If one of the subgraphs, H_1 say, contains the 2-edge RY, but neither of the loops, then it cannot contain the 2-edge GY; so it must contain the 4-edge GY and the 1-edge RG (to satisfy property (c) at G). But this means that, by property (c), neither R nor Y can be incident with a 3-edge, contradicting property (a). It follows that neither subgraph can contain the 2-edge RY.

So both H_1 and H_2 must be subgraphs of the graph shown on the right.

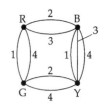

The result now follows by considering the possible cases that can occur. By property (a), each of H_1 and H_2 must contain one 1-edge and one 2-edge. There are just two possible ways of doing this, and satisfying property (b):

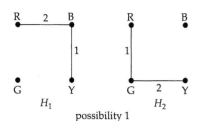

possibility 1

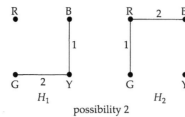

possibility 2

In possibility 1, both possible positions for a 3-edge in H_1 are already taken; so possibility 1 does not lead to a solution. Possibility 2, however, leads to the unique pair of subgraphs satisfying properties (a), (b) and (c) shown on the right.

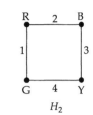

1.10 C_3H_8, has 11 vertices and 10 edges.

C_4H_{10} has 14 vertices and 13 edges.

C_5H_{12} has 17 vertices and 16 edges.

In each case, the graph of the molecule is a connected graph in which the number of vertices exceeds the number of edges by 1.

As we shall see in *Graphs 2, Trees,* this means that the graph of the molecule is a tree.

1.11 The paths corresponding to these key-changes have lengths:

(a) 4;   (b) 4;   (c) 3;   (d) 5.

Key-change (c) is thus the least remote.

1.12

(a) The signed graph is balanced, since we can colour its vertices black or white in such a way that positive edges have ends of the same colour and negative edges have ends of different colours, as shown.

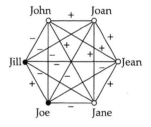

(b) Let *G* be any balanced signed graph. Since *G* is balanced, we can colour its vertices black and white so that every negative edge has a black end and a white end. If we now proceed around any cycle, there is a change of colour whenever we traverse a negative edge. Since the final colour must be the same as the first one, there must be an even number of colour changes. Hence there must be an even number of negative edges in any cycle.

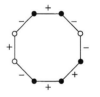

2.1 We use Theorems 2.1 and 2.2.

(a) K_n is Eulerian only when *n* is odd, since each vertex degree is $n - 1$;
K_n is semi-Eulerian only when $n = 2$.

(b) $K_{r,s}$ is Eulerian only when *r* and *s* are both even, since each vertex degree is either *r* or *s*;
$K_{r,s}$ is semi-Eulerian when $r = s = 1$ or when one of *r* and *s* is 2 and the other is odd.

(c) C_n is Eulerian for all values of *n*, since each vertex degree is 2;
C_n is never semi-Eulerian.

(d) Q_n is Eulerian when *n* is even, since each vertex degree is *n*;
Q_n is semi-Eulerian only when $n = 1$.

2.2 The five ways of splitting the graph into disjoint cycles are:

abca, cdec, aefa;   *abcdefa, acea;*   *abcefa, acdea;*
abcdea, acefa;   *acdefa, abcea.*

2.3 Such graphs do not exist, since the number of vertices of odd degree is always even.

See Problem 1.12(a).

2.4

(a) K_n is Hamiltonian for all $n \geq 3$;

   K_n is semi-Hamiltonian only for $n = 2$.

(b) $K_{r,s}$ is Hamiltonian whenever $r = s$ and $r \geq 2$;

   $K_{r,s}$ is semi-Hamiltonian when r and s differ by 1 or when $r = s = 1$.

$K_{2,3}$, for example, was considered in Problem 2.13(a).

(c) C_n is Hamiltonian for all values of n;

   C_n is never semi-Hamiltonian.

(d) Q_n is Hamiltonian for all values of $n \geq 2$;

   Q_n is semi-Hamiltonian only for $n = 1$.

2.5 The conditions of Ore's theorem hold for graph (a); in this case, $\deg v + \deg w \geq 5$ for each pair of non-adjacent vertices v and w.

The conditions of Ore's theorem do not hold for graph (b); in this case, there are two pairs of non-adjacent vertices v, w such that $\deg v + \deg w = 4$.

2.6

(a) Suppose that v and w are non-adjacent vertices of G with $\deg v + \deg w \leq n - 1$. Let us now compute the maximum possible number of edges in G.

   If each vertex were joined to every other, then G would be the complete graph K_n with $n(n-1)/2$ edges. This would include $2(n-1) - 1$ edges adjacent to v or w, since each of v and w would be adjacent to $n - 1$ other vertices and since the edge vw must not be counted twice. But we are assuming that $\deg v + \deg w \leq n - 1$. Therefore the total number of edges is *at most*

$$\frac{n(n-1)}{2} - [2(n-1) - 1] + (n-1) \quad = \frac{n-1}{2}(n - 4 + 2) + 1$$

$$= \frac{(n-1)(n-2)}{2} + 1.$$

   But G has $(n-1)(n-2)/2 + 2$ edges, so we have a contradiction. Therefore $\deg v + \deg w \geq n$ for each pair of non-adjacent vertices of G, and so by Ore's theorem G is Hamiltonian.

(b) Take the graph obtained by adjoining a single vertex by an edge to K_{n-1}.

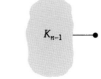

K_{n-1}

2.7

(a) Three, since there are six vertices of odd degree.

See Problem 2.15.

(b) Five, since there are ten vertices of odd degree.

2.8 The quickest way to prove this result is to look at the two squares indicated below.

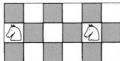

The only possible knight's moves from these two squares are as follows:

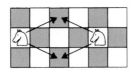

But the corresponding edges form a cycle, and so it is impossible to include them as part of a full tour. Thus, no knight's tour is possible on a 3×6 chessboard.

3.1

(a) (2) is false; (1) and (3) are true.

(b) outdeg $u = 2$, outdeg $v = 0$, outdeg $w = 3$, outdeg $x = 2$, and indeg $u = 2$, indeg $v = 2$, indeg $w = 1$, indeg $x = 2$, and so the sum of the out-degrees and the sum of the in-degrees are both 7. There are seven arcs, and so the sum of the out-degrees and the sum of the in-degrees are each equal to the number of arcs, as required.

(c) (1) There are various possibilities — for example, the walk with arcs 5, 3, 7, 4, 5, 6, 5.

  (2) length 1: the loop 7;

    length 2: the multiple arcs 5 and 6;

    length 3: the triangle with arcs 3, 4, 5;

    length 4: none.

  (3) As there are only four vertices, no path can have length greater than 3; a path of length 3 is $xuwv$, with arcs 4, 5, 2.

3.2 Digraphs (b) and (d) are the same;

digraph (c) is isomorphic to (b) and (d), as can be seen by interchanging the labels 1 and 4;

digraph (a) is not isomorphic to any of the other three, since it alone contains a vertex, 2, with out-degree 3.

3.3 K_5 and the Petersen graph can be oriented as follows:

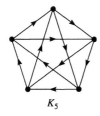 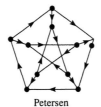

K_5 Petersen

The following graph cannot be oriented, because of the 'bridge' in the middle:

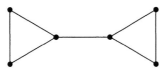

3.4 Digraph (a) is Eulerian, but not Hamiltonian.

Digraph (b) is Hamiltonian, but not Eulerian.

3.5

(a) length 3: $uvxu$, $uywu$, $uyxu$, $vxwv$, $vywv$;

  length 4: $uvxwu$, $uvywu$, $uvyxu$, $uyxwu$, $vyxwv$;

  length 5: $uvyxwu$, $uywvxu$;

(b) possibilities include $uvyxwuywvxu$ and $uyxuvxwvywu$;

(c) the only two are the cycles of length 5 you found in part (a), namely $uvyxwu$ and $uywvxu$.

3.6 Cycles (a) and (b) are negative feedback cycles; cycle (c) is a positive feedback cycle.

3.7 There are four tournaments with four vertices:

out-degree sequence: (0,1,2,3)   (0,2,2,2)   (1,1,1,3)   (1,1,2,2)

Only in the first of these is a *unique* ranking possible.

4.1

$$\begin{bmatrix} 0 & 1 & 0 & 0 & 1 \\ 1 & 0 & 1 & 0 & 1 \\ 0 & 1 & 0 & 1 & 0 \\ 0 & 0 & 1 & 0 & 1 \\ 1 & 1 & 0 & 1 & 0 \end{bmatrix} \qquad \begin{bmatrix} 0 & 0 & 0 & 0 & 0 \\ 0 & 0 & 1 & 0 & 1 \\ 0 & 0 & 0 & 1 & 0 \\ 0 & 0 & 0 & 0 & 0 \\ 0 & 1 & 0 & 1 & 0 \end{bmatrix}$$

(a)   (b)

4.2

$$\begin{bmatrix} 1 & 1 & 0 & 0 & 0 & 0 \\ 0 & 1 & 1 & 0 & 0 & 1 \\ 0 & 0 & 1 & 1 & 0 & 0 \\ 0 & 0 & 0 & 1 & 1 & 0 \\ 1 & 0 & 0 & 0 & 1 & 1 \end{bmatrix} \qquad \begin{bmatrix} 1 & 0 & 0 & 1 & 0 \\ -1 & 1 & 0 & 0 & 1 \\ 0 & -1 & -1 & 0 & 0 \\ 0 & 0 & 1 & -1 & -1 \end{bmatrix}$$

(a)   (b)

4.3

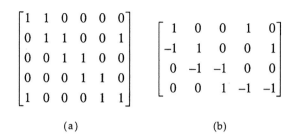

(a)   (b)

4.4

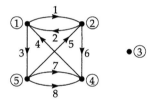

4.5

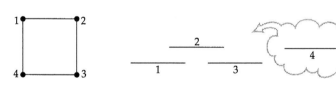

The intervals corresponding to vertices 1 and 3 do not overlap, and the interval corresponding to vertex 2 overlaps both of these intervals, as shown above. But it is now impossible to insert the interval corresponding to vertex 4, as such an interval must overlap intervals 1 and 3 without overlapping interval 2. Thus C_4 is not an interval graph.

4.6

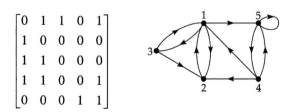

$$\begin{bmatrix} 0 & 1 & 1 & 0 & 1 \\ 1 & 0 & 0 & 0 & 0 \\ 1 & 1 & 0 & 0 & 0 \\ 1 & 1 & 0 & 0 & 1 \\ 0 & 0 & 0 & 1 & 1 \end{bmatrix}$$

The corresponding Markov chain is irreducible, as there is a path from any vertex to any other.

Solutions to the problems

Solution 1.1

(a) vertices: $\{a, b, c, d\}$
edges: $\{ab, ad, bc, bd, cc, cd\}$
It is not a simple graph, because there is a loop at the vertex c.

(b) vertices: $\{0, 1, 2, 3, 4, 5, 6, 7, 8, 9\}$
edges: $\{01, 04, 05, 12, 16, 23, 27, 34, 38, 49, 57, 58, 68, 69, 79\}$
It is a simple graph.

Solution 1.2

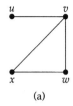 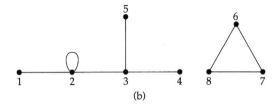

(a)   (b)

Graph (a) is a simple graph. Graph (b) is not a simple graph, because there is a loop at the vertex 2.

Solution 1.3

(a) yes; (b) no; (c) yes; (d) no.

Solution 1.4

(a) To show that the graphs are isomorphic, we must match up:

the vertices with a loop: 3 and e;
the vertices where four edges meet: 1 and c;
the vertices where three edges meet: 5 and b;
the remaining vertices of the 'triangles': 4 and a;
the other two vertices: 2 and d.

Thus, to show that the graphs are isomorphic, we must use the one–one correspondence:

1	2	3	4	5
↕	↕	↕	↕	↕
c	d	e	a	b

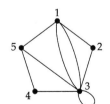 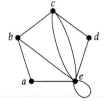 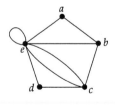

(b) To show that the graphs are isomorphic, we must match up:

the vertices where three edges meet;
the vertices where two edges meet.

Thus $\{q, s\}$ must correspond to $\{+, -\}$;
and $\{p, r, t\}$ must correspond to $\{\times, =, \div\}$.

There are no other constraints. Thus, to show that the graphs are isomorphic, we can use the one–one correspondence:

p	q	r	s	t
↕	↕	↕	↕	↕
$\times$	$+$	$=$	$-$	$\div$

In drawing graphs, it is not easy to know initially where best to place the vertices and edges. The usual approach is to draw a rough sketch and then to reposition the vertices and edges so that, where possible, edges do not cross and the graph is easy to interpret. In solutions that involve drawing graphs, it is unlikely that, at first, your drawings will look like ours; but you should be able to see how to reposition the vertices and edges so that you can derive ours from yours. By the end of the unit, however, you should have gained sufficient experience in drawing graphs for your drawings to resemble ours rather more closely.

We can do this in 2 ways.
We can do this in 6 ways.

There are eleven other possible matchings.

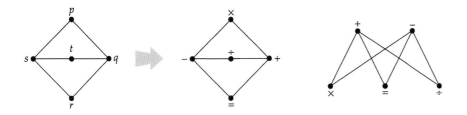

Solution 1.5

No, they are not isomorphic. One way of seeing this is to look at the four vertices where just two edges meet — in the first graph they are the vertices 3, 4, 7 and 8, which are adjacent in pairs, whereas in the second graph they are b, d, f and h, and none is adjacent to any other.

Solution 1.6

One possible labelling is as follows:

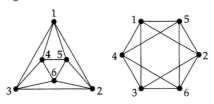

Solution 1.7

Graphs (a) and (b) are subgraphs of G; graph (c) is not a subgraph of G, as it contains the edges uw and vx, which are not edges of G.

Solution 1.8

Graph (c) is a subgraph of H; graphs (a) and (b) are not.

Solution 1.9

The eleven unlabelled simple graphs with four vertices are as follows:

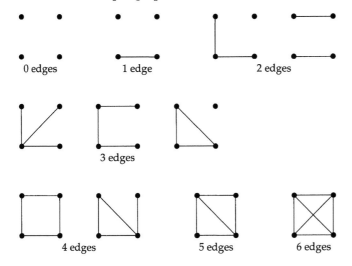

Solution 1.10

The degree sequences are:

(a) $(1, 1, 1, 1, 1, 1, 2, 4, 4)$; (b) $(4, 4, 4, 4, 4)$ (c) $(0, 1, 3, 4, 4, 5, 5)$.

Solution 1.11

In (a), the number of edges is 8 and the sum of the vertex degrees is 16. In (b), the number of edges is 10 and the sum of the vertex degrees is 20. In (c), the number of edges is 11 and the sum of the vertex degrees is 22.

In each case the sum of the vertex degrees is exactly twice the number of edges; the reason for this is given in the following text.

Solution 1.12

(a) For any graph, the handshaking lemma holds, so that the sum of the vertex degrees is twice the number of edges, and is thus an even number. If the number of vertices of odd degree were odd, then the sum of the vertex degrees would be an odd number, giving a contradiction. So the number of vertices of odd degree must be even.

(b) The three graphs (a), (b) and (c) have, respectively, 6, 0 and 4 vertices of odd degree, and these are all even numbers.

Solution 1.13

There are various possibilities — for example:

$r = 3$ $r = 4$ $r = 5$

Solution 1.14

(a) $n = 5, r = 2$, so the number of edges is $(5 \times 2)/2 = 5$;

(b) $n = 10, r = 3$, so the number of edges is $(10 \times 3)/2 = 15$;

(c) $n = 12, r = 5$, so the number of edges is $(12 \times 5)/2 = 30$.

You can check that these numbers are correct by counting the edges in each case.

Solution 1.15

(a) If such a graph existed it would have an odd number of vertices of odd degree, contradicting the result of Problem 1.12(a).
Alternatively, such a graph would have $(7 \times 3)/2 = 10\frac{1}{2}$ edges, which is impossible. Thus no such graph exists.

(b) If such a graph existed it would have an odd number of vertices of odd degree, contradicting the result of Problem 1.12(a).
Alternatively, such a graph would have $nr/2$ edges; since n and r are odd, so is nr, and hence $nr/2$ is not an integer, which is impossible. Thus no such graph exists.

Solution 1.16

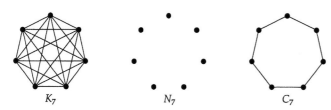

K_7 N_7 C_7

These graphs have, respectively, 21, 0 and 7 edges.

Solution 1.17

(a) trail, 5, x, y;   (b) path, 3, u, z.

Note that alternative answers are possible; for example, we could have given the answer *walk* in each case.

Solution 1.18

length 3:   *stzy*;   length 4:   *stzxy* and *svtzy*;

length 5:   *stzwxy*, *svtzxy* and *svutzy*;   length 6:   *svutzxy* and *svtzwxy*;

length 7:   *svutzwxy*.

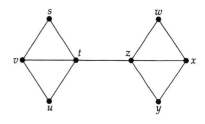

Solution 1.19

There are various possibilities — for example:

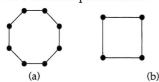 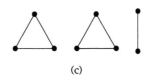

(a) (b) (c)

Solution 1.20

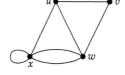

(a) There are various possibilities — for example, *uvu* or *uvwuxwu*.

(b) Again, there are various possibilities — for example, *uwxxu*.

(c) length 1: the loop *xx*;

　　　length 2: the multiple edges *wxw*;

　　　length 3: the triangle *uvwu*, and both of the triangles *uwxu*;

　　　length 4: both of the 'quadrilaterals' *uvwxu*.

Solution 1.21

Let G be a bipartite graph. If we colour the vertices of G black and white, then the vertices in each cycle must alternate between these two colours. This implies that the number of edges in each cycle must be even.

Solution 1.22

(a) There are various possible drawings — for example:

 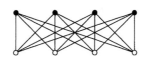

These graphs have, respectively: 5 vertices and 6 edges; 8 vertices and 7 edges; 8 vertices and 16 edges.

(b) r and s must be equal.

Solution 1.23

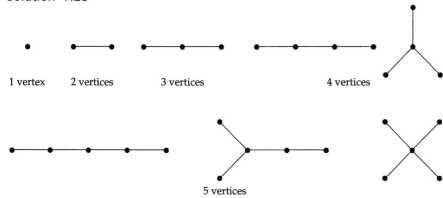

1 vertex　　2 vertices　　3 vertices　　4 vertices

5 vertices

Solution 1.24

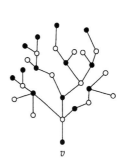

(a) Choose any vertex v in a tree T and colour it black. Colour all vertices adjacent to v white. Next, colour all uncoloured vertices adjacent to these black. Continue this process until every vertex has been coloured.

Since T is a tree, there is just one path between any two vertices. Thus, by the way we coloured the vertices, no two adjacent vertices have the same colour. So T is bipartite.

(b) Every tree can be built up from a single vertex by successively adding an edge and a new vertex, as often as necessary. At each stage we increase the number of vertices by 1 and the number of edges by 1. Since we start with 1 vertex and 0 edges, we must end up with n vertices and $n - 1$ edges.

Solution 1.25

Using the method described in the text, we obtain the superimposed graph G shown in the margin.

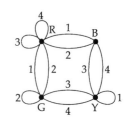

A pair of subgraphs H_1 and H_2 and a corresponding solution are then as follows:

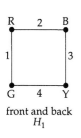

front and back
H_1

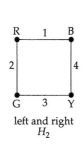

left and right
H_2

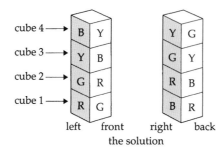

the solution

There are several other solutions.

Solution 1.26

(a)

(b)

Solution 1.27

The paths corresponding to these key-changes have lengths:

(a) 3;   (b) 4;   (c) 3;   (d) 2.

Key-change (d) is thus the least remote.

Solution 1.28

Only the signed graphs (a) and (c) are balanced. The corresponding bipartite graphs are shown in the margin.

(a)   (c)

In each case where Eulerian trails or Hamiltonian cycles exist, there are several alternative trails/cycles.

Solution 2.1

	Eulerian?	Eulerian trail	Hamiltonian?	Hamiltonian cycle
(a)	no	—	yes	abcda
(b)	yes	abcdeacebda	yes	abcdea
(c)	no	—	yes	abfehgcda
(d)	yes	abcadcfbefdea	yes	abcdfea
(e)	no	—	no	—
(f)	no	—	yes	adbecfa
(g)	no	—	yes	abcda

Solution 2.2

(a) If an Eulerian trail exists in a graph, then, whenever you go into a vertex, you must be able to leave it by another edge. It follows that each time you pass through a vertex you contribute 2 to the degree of that vertex. (This is also true of the first and last edges, which contribute 2 to the degree of the starting vertex.) So, in an Eulerian graph, each vertex degree must be a sum of 2s — that is, an even number.

(b)   The rule is:

> to show that a given connected graph is Eulerian, demonstrate that all the vertices have even degree;
> to show that a given connected graph is not Eulerian, exhibit just *one* vertex of odd degree.

For the graphs in Problem 2.1, we have:

graph (a) has vertex degrees 3, 3, 3, 3, so (a) is not Eulerian;
graph (b) has vertex degrees 4, 4, 4, 4, 4, so (b) is Eulerian;
graph (c) has vertex degrees 3, 3, 3, 3, 3, 3, 3, 3, so (c) is not Eulerian;
graph (d) has vertex degrees 4, 4, 4, 4, 4, 4, so (d) is Eulerian;
graph (e) has vertex degrees 3, 3, 2, 2, 2, so (e) is not Eulerian;
graph (f) has vertex degrees 3, 3, 3, 3, 3, 3, so (f) is not Eulerian;
graph (g) has vertex degrees 3, 3, 3, 5, so (g) is not Eulerian.

In cases (a), (c), (e), (f) and (g) it would have been sufficient to exhibit just one vertex of odd degree.

Solution 2.3

(a) K_8 is not Eulerian, since it is regular of degree 7;

(b) $K_{8,8}$ is Eulerian, since it is regular of degree 8;

(c) C_8 is Eulerian, since it is regular of degree 2;

(d)   the dodecahedron graph is not Eulerian, since it is regular of degree 3;

(e) Q_8 is Eulerian, since it is regular of degree 8.

Solution 2.4

There are many possibilities. For example, if we take the Eulerian trail 01234024130, and add the doubles in a suitable way, we get the ring shown.

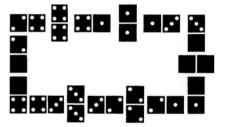

Solution 2.5

Graph (a) is semi-Eulerian, since a and b are the only vertices of odd degree; a suitable open trail is $acbdaeb$, starting at a and ending at b.

Graph (b) is not semi-Eulerian, since it has four vertices of odd degree.

Graph (c) is semi-Eulerian, since the only vertices of odd degree are w and z; a suitable open trail is $wxyzuvwyuwzvxz$.

Solution 2.6

The following graph models this problem:

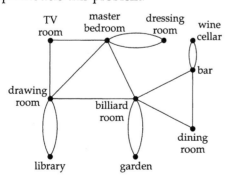

This graph is semi-Eulerian. There is only one semi-Eulerian trail — between the drawing room and the master bedroom, since these are the only vertices of odd degree. This implies that it is impossible to enter the house, go through each door exactly once, and then leave the house. So the gardener lied — but this does not prove that the gardener killed the Count. Indeed, the only way that Hercules Parrot could know who murdered the Count, given the information available, is if he committed the terrible crime himself!

Solution 2.7

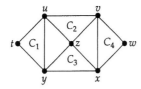

There is only one possibility — the cycles C_1, C_2, C_3 and C_4.

If we trace around C_1, 'picking up' C_2 and C_3 as we go, we get the closed trail *tuvzuyzxyt*. This trail misses out C_4, which can be inserted, on tracing round this trail, at the vertex v, to give the Eulerian trail *tuvwxvzuyzxyt*.

Solution 2.8

There are two such Hamiltonian cycles:

$$JVTSRWXZQPNMLKFDCBGHJ;$$

$$JVTSRWXHGFDCBZQPNMLKJ.$$

Note that the letter after R must be W, since otherwise W would have to be omitted.

Solution 2.9

There is only one such path — *BCDFGHXZQPNMLKJVWRST*.

Solution 2.10

(a) The graph $K_{4,4}$ is Hamiltonian; a suitable Hamiltonian cycle is *ahbgcfdea*.

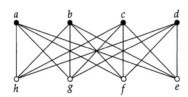

(b) A tree does not contain a cycle, so the only tree that is Hamiltonian is the trivial tree with one vertex and no edges.

Solution 2.11

(a) The vertices of any bipartite graph can be split into two sets A and B in such a way that each edge has one end in A and one end in B. Any Hamiltonian cycle must alternate between these two sets, ending in the same set as it started. It follows that if a bipartite graph is Hamiltonian then the sets A and B must have the same number of vertices. This is impossible if the total number of vertices is odd.

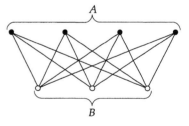

(b) This graph is a bipartite graph with an odd number of vertices, and so cannot be Hamiltonian, by part (a).

Solution 2.12

(a) If $\deg v \geq n/2$ for each vertex v, then $\deg v + \deg w \geq n$ for each pair of vertices v and w, whether adjacent or not. The result now follows from Ore's theorem.

(b) Any cycle graph C_n, where $n \geq 5$, is Hamiltonian, but does not satisfy the conditions of Ore's theorem, because each vertex has degree 2.

Solution 2.13

Graph (a) is semi-Hamiltonian — a suitable path is *cadbe*.

Graph (b) is Hamiltonian — a suitable cycle is *abcda* — and so is not semi-Hamiltonian.

Graph (c) is Hamiltonian — a suitable cycle is *vwxyuzv* — and so is not semi-Hamiltonian.

Solution 2.14

There are exactly four vertices of odd degree, so at least two continuous pen-strokes are required; in fact, two are sufficient.

Solution 2.15

If we add $k/2$ edges to G, joining the k vertices of odd degree in pairs, we get a new graph G' in which each vertex has even degree. It follows that G' contains an Eulerian trail.

If we now draw this trail, and then omit the added edges, we get the required $k/2$ pen-strokes.

Solution 2.16

The graph of knight's moves associated with any chessboard is bipartite, since a knight's move always takes a knight to a square of a different colour, and so we can take A to be the set of black squares and B to be the set of white squares. The result now follows immediately from the fact that bipartite graphs with an odd number of vertices cannot be Hamiltonian. (All we are saying is that, since a knight always moves from a black square to a white square, or vice versa, the number of black squares must equal the number of white squares. But this is impossible for any board with an odd number of squares.)

Solution 2.17

All we need to do is to find another Hamiltonian cycle in the 4-cube. One possibility is

$$0000 \to 0100 \to 1100 \to 1110 \to 1111 \to 1011 \to 0011 \to 0001 \to$$
$$1001 \to 1101 \to 0101 \to 0111 \to 0110 \to 0010 \to 1010 \to 1000 \to 0000.$$

Solution 3.1

(a) vertices: $\{a, b, c, d\}$
    arcs: $\{ba, bd, cb, da, db, dc\}$
    It is a simple digraph.

Note that, although arcs bd and db both join the same pair of vertices, they are not multiple arcs as they are in different directions.

(b) vertices: $\{0, 1, 2, 3, 4\}$
    arcs: $\{10, 12, 32, 40, 43\}$
    It is a simple digraph.

Solution 3.2

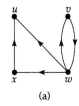

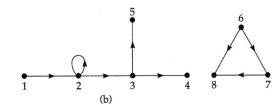

(a)   (b)

Digraph (a) is a simple digraph. Digraph (b) is not a simple digraph, because it contains a loop at the vertex 2.

Solution 3.3

(a) no; (b) yes; (c) yes.

Solution 3.4

To show that the digraphs are isomorphic, we must match up:

  the vertices with a loop: c and 1;
  the vertices where six arcs meet: d and 3;
  the vertices where five arcs meet: a and 2;
  the other two vertices: b and 4.

Thus, to show that the two digraphs are isomorphic, we must use the one–one correspondence:

a	b	c	d
$\updownarrow$	$\updownarrow$	$\updownarrow$	$\updownarrow$
2	4	1	3

Solution 3.5

No, they are not isomorphic. One way of seeing this is to notice that the second digraph has a vertex with three emerging arcs (vertex 1), whereas the first digraph has no such vertex. Another way is to notice that the first digraph has a 'directed triangle' ($a \rightarrow b \rightarrow c \rightarrow a$), whereas the second digraph has no such triangle.

Solution 3.6

One possible labelling is as follows:

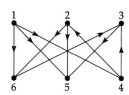 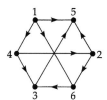

Solution 3.7

Digraph (a) is a subdigraph of D; digraph (b) is not, as it contains the arc xv, which is not an arc of D; digraph (c) is not, as it contains the arc ux, for example, which is not an arc of D.

Solution 3.8

Digraphs (a) and (b) are subdigraphs of C; digraph (c) is not.

Solution 3.9

(a) out-degree sequence: (0, 1, 1, 1, 1, 1, 1, 1, 1);
     in-degree sequence: (0, 0, 0, 0, 0, 0, 1, 3, 4);

(b) out-degree sequence: (1, 2, 2, 2, 3);
     in-degree sequence: (1, 2, 2, 2, 3);

(c) out-degree sequence: (1, 1, 2, 2, 2, 3);
     in-degree sequence: (0, 0, 2, 3, 3, 3).

Solution 3.10

In digraph (a), the number of arcs is 8 and the sum of the out-degrees and the sum of the in-degrees are both 8.
In digraph (b), the number of arcs is 10 and the sum of the out-degrees and the sum of the in-degrees are both 10.
In digraph (c), the number of arcs is 11 and the sum of the out-degrees and the sum of the in-degrees are both 11.

In each case, the sum of the out-degrees and the sum of the in-degrees are both equal to the number of arcs; the reason for this is given in the following text.

Solution 3.11

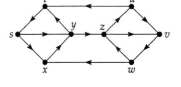

(a) length 5: *tsyzvw;*
     length 6: *tsxyzvw* and *tsyzuvw;*
     length 7: *tsxyzuvw;*

(b) length 3: *wxyt* and *wzut;*
     length 5: *wxyzut;*

(c) There are two possibilities: *tsyzvwxyt* and *tsyzvwzut.*

(d) Any cycle containing both *t* and *w* must consist of a path from *t* to *w* followed by a path from *w* to *t*. But all paths from *t* to *w* contain both *y* and *z* (by part (a)), and all paths from *w* to *t* contain *y* or *z* (by part (b)), so that either *y* or *z* must occur twice. Since this is not allowed, there can be no cycle containing both *t* and *w*.

Solution 3.12

(a) connected, but not strongly connected (since there are no paths from the centre vertex to any other);

(b) strongly connected;

(c) disconnected;

(d) connected, but not strongly connected (since, for example, there are no paths from the top right-hand vertex to any other).

Solution 3.13

	Eulerian?	Eulerian trail	Hamiltonian?	Hamiltonian cycle
(a)	no	—	yes	*abdca*
(b)	yes	*abdecdacbea*	yes	*abecda*
(c)	no	—	yes	*abecda*

Solution 3.14

(a) A digraph is Eulerian if and only if the out-degree and in-degree of each vertex are equal.

(b) Since there is no vertex whose out-degree and in-degree are equal, digraph (a) is not Eulerian.

In digraph (b), the out-degree and in-degree of each vertex are equal, and the digraph is therefore Eulerian.

In digraph (c), the out-degree and in-degree of the vertices *a* and *e* are not equal, and so this digraph is not Eulerian.

Solution 3.15

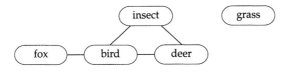

Solution 3.16

Positive feedback cycle: *cefhgc.*

Negative feedback cycles: *ghg, ahga, abdfhga, ceifhgc.*

Solution 3.17

Another Eulerian trail is

$$101 \rightarrow 010 \rightarrow 100 \rightarrow 001 \rightarrow 011 \rightarrow 110 \rightarrow 100 \rightarrow 000 \rightarrow$$
$$000 \rightarrow 001 \rightarrow 010 \rightarrow 101 \rightarrow 011 \rightarrow 111 \rightarrow 111 \rightarrow 110 \rightarrow 101.$$

This can be compressed to give the 16-bit sequence

1010011000010111.

This leads to the solution to the rotating drum problem for sixteen divisions shown in the margin.

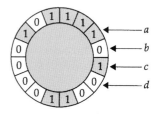

Solution 3.18

Five: *abecd, bcaed, becad, cabed, ecabd*.

Solution 4.1

$$
\begin{array}{c c}
\begin{array}{c}
\ 1\ \ 2\ \ 3\ \ 4\ \ 5 \\
\begin{array}{c}1\\2\\3\\4\\5\end{array}
\begin{bmatrix}
0 & 1 & 0 & 0 & 1 \\
1 & 0 & 1 & 3 & 0 \\
0 & 1 & 0 & 1 & 0 \\
0 & 3 & 1 & 0 & 1 \\
1 & 0 & 0 & 1 & 0
\end{bmatrix}\\
(a)
\end{array}
&
\begin{array}{c}
\ 1\ \ 2\ \ 3\ \ 4\ \ 5 \\
\begin{array}{c}1\\2\\3\\4\\5\end{array}
\begin{bmatrix}
0 & 1 & 0 & 0 & 1 \\
1 & 0 & 0 & 2 & 1 \\
0 & 0 & 0 & 0 & 0 \\
0 & 2 & 0 & 0 & 1 \\
1 & 1 & 0 & 1 & 0
\end{bmatrix}\\
(b)
\end{array}
\end{array}
$$

Solution 4.2

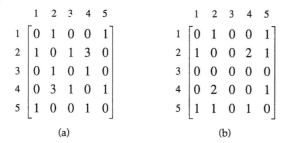

(a)   (b)

Solution 4.3

$$
\begin{array}{c c}
\begin{array}{c}
\ 1\ \ 2\ \ 3\ \ 4\ \ 5 \\
\begin{array}{c}1\\2\\3\\4\\5\end{array}
\begin{bmatrix}
0 & 1 & 0 & 0 & 0 \\
0 & 0 & 1 & 1 & 0 \\
0 & 0 & 0 & 0 & 0 \\
0 & 2 & 1 & 0 & 0 \\
1 & 0 & 0 & 1 & 0
\end{bmatrix}\\
(a)
\end{array}
&
\begin{array}{c}
\ 1\ \ 2\ \ 3\ \ 4\ \ 5 \\
\begin{array}{c}1\\2\\3\\4\\5\end{array}
\begin{bmatrix}
0 & 0 & 0 & 1 & 0 \\
1 & 0 & 0 & 0 & 0 \\
1 & 1 & 0 & 1 & 0 \\
1 & 0 & 0 & 0 & 1 \\
1 & 0 & 0 & 0 & 0
\end{bmatrix}\\
(b)
\end{array}
\end{array}
$$

Solution 4.4

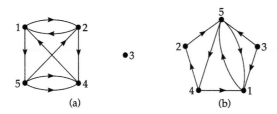

(a)   (b)

Solution 4.5

$$
\begin{array}{c}
\ 1\ \ 2\ \ 3\ \ 4\ \ 5\ \ 6\ \ 7\ \ 8 \\
\begin{array}{c}①\\②\\③\\④\\⑤\end{array}
\begin{bmatrix}
1 & 0 & 0 & 0 & 1 & 0 & 0 & 0 \\
1 & 1 & 0 & 0 & 0 & 1 & 1 & 1 \\
0 & 1 & 1 & 0 & 0 & 0 & 0 & 0 \\
0 & 0 & 1 & 1 & 0 & 1 & 1 & 1 \\
0 & 0 & 0 & 1 & 1 & 0 & 0 & 0
\end{bmatrix}\\
(a)
\end{array}
\qquad
\begin{array}{c}
\ 1\ \ 2\ \ 3\ \ 4\ \ 5\ \ 6\ \ 7 \\
\begin{array}{c}①\\②\\③\\④\end{array}
\begin{bmatrix}
1 & 0 & 0 & 0 & 0 & 1 & 1 \\
1 & 1 & 1 & 1 & 0 & 0 & 0 \\
0 & 1 & 1 & 1 & 1 & 0 & 1 \\
0 & 0 & 0 & 0 & 1 & 1 & 0
\end{bmatrix}\\
(b)
\end{array}
$$

Solution 4.6

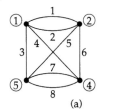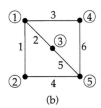

(a)　　　　(b)

Solution 4.7

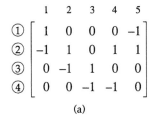

$$
\begin{array}{c c c c c c}
 & 1 & 2 & 3 & 4 & 5 \\
① & 1 & 0 & 0 & 0 & -1 \\
② & -1 & 1 & 0 & 1 & 1 \\
③ & 0 & -1 & 1 & 0 & 0 \\
④ & 0 & 0 & -1 & -1 & 0
\end{array}
$$

(a)

$$
\begin{array}{c c c c c c c c c}
 & 1 & 2 & 3 & 4 & 5 & 6 & 7 & 8 \\
① & 1 & 0 & 0 & 0 & -1 & 0 & 0 & 0 \\
② & -1 & 1 & 0 & 0 & 0 & 1 & -1 & -1 \\
③ & 0 & -1 & -1 & 0 & 0 & 0 & 0 & 0 \\
④ & 0 & 0 & 1 & -1 & 0 & -1 & 1 & 1 \\
⑤ & 0 & 0 & 0 & 1 & 1 & 0 & 0 & 0
\end{array}
$$

(b)

Solution 4.8

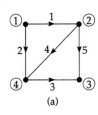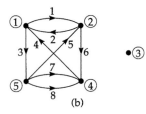

(a)　　　　(b)

Solution 4.9

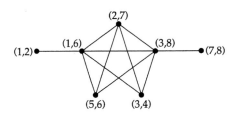

Solution 4.10

(a)

$$
\begin{bmatrix}
1 & 0 & 0 & 0 & 0 & 0 \\
\frac{1}{2} & \frac{1}{6} & \frac{1}{3} & 0 & 0 & 0 \\
0 & \frac{1}{2} & \frac{1}{6} & \frac{1}{3} & 0 & 0 \\
0 & 0 & \frac{1}{2} & \frac{1}{6} & \frac{1}{3} & 0 \\
0 & 0 & 0 & \frac{1}{2} & \frac{1}{6} & \frac{1}{3} \\
0 & 0 & 0 & 0 & 1 & 0
\end{bmatrix}
$$

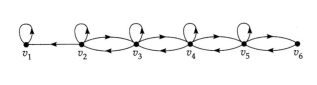

The associated digraph is not strongly connected, as there is no arc out of v_1 to another vertex, and so the resulting Markov chain is not irreducible.

(b)

$$
\begin{bmatrix}
0 & 1 & 0 & 0 & 0 & 0 \\
\frac{1}{2} & \frac{1}{6} & \frac{1}{3} & 0 & 0 & 0 \\
0 & \frac{1}{2} & \frac{1}{6} & \frac{1}{3} & 0 & 0 \\
0 & 0 & \frac{1}{2} & \frac{1}{6} & \frac{1}{3} & 0 \\
0 & 0 & 0 & \frac{1}{2} & \frac{1}{6} & \frac{1}{3} \\
0 & 0 & 0 & 0 & 1 & 0
\end{bmatrix}
$$

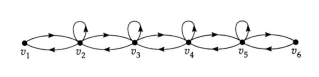

The associated digraph is strongly connected, and so the resulting Markov chain is irreducible.

Index